The Road to Grace for Couples

A WORKBOOK FOR HEALING FROM PORN AND ADULTERY

MIKE GENUNG

Blazing Grace Publishing ✦ Colorado Springs, CO

BLAZING GRACE PUBLISHING
PO Box 25763
Colorado Springs, CO 80936
www.roadtograce.net

The Road to Grace for Couples:
A Workbook for Healing from Porn and Adultery

©2016 by Mike Genung

Scripture quotations taken from the New American Standard Bible®, Copyright ©1960, 1962, 1963, 1968, 1971, 1972, 1973, 1975, 1977, 1995 by The Lockman Foundation. Used by permission.
www.Lockman.org

Cover design ©2016 TLC Graphics, www.TLCGraphics.com

Interior design by Williams Writing, Editing & Design,
www.williamswriting.com

ISBN-13: 978-0-9787756-8-1
ISBN-10: 0-9787756-8-6
SAN: 851-6022

Printed in USA

More copies of this book can be ordered at www.roadtograce.net.

CONTENTS

INTRODUCTION

It breaks my heart when I hear that a couple is divorcing because of porn or adultery.

It grieves me because I know the pain and trauma porn and adultery inflict on a marriage, especially for the wife, as I wounded my wife Michelle with my sexual sin. I also know what divorce does to the kids, having watched my parents end their marriage years ago.

It makes me angry, because I know many marriages could be saved but won't be, because churches won't talk about sex or porn, and some well-meaning counselors are doing more harm than good. I've heard of wives that were told "you're not giving your husband enough sex so he's masturbating to porn." Insanity. A woman could have the perfect body (there is no such thing) and have sex with her husband three times a day (as if he could) but it would never resolve his lust-craving.

Sharing with friends and family is risky. One wife whose marriage recovered told me she had to distance herself from most of her friends because they kept pouring gasoline on the fire of her anger rather than helping her find ways to reconcile with her husband.

Recovering from porn, adultery, or other forms of sexual sin is one of the most painful, difficult, and challenging paths to walk for a couple. The husband must break free from the bondage of sexual sin; a confusing and intimidating path that requires him to press through shame and fear, confront his pride, sex, and self-absorption, and resolve the distorted core beliefs that triggered lust, while his wife processes all of her pain, anger, shock, and sorrow, learns to trust again, and gropes her way to forgiveness.

Add in the everyday stress of work and family, the normal disagreements that arise in marriage, and an invisible enemy, Satan, who is attacking them with everything he has, and you'll find yourself facing the Mount Everest of marital challenges.

The journey is often confusing and frustrating.

A husband feels a sense of victory after having received a coin from his support group commemorating three months of sexual purity. He rushes home, eager to tell his wife: "Surely she will be happy." When he shows his coin to her, she breaks down crying. His victory celebration salted her wound; the pain is overwhelming her again. She didn't sign up for marriage to a sex and porn addict, and explodes: "Three months? You shouldn't have used porn once while we've been married! Is this supposed to make me feel better?!"

Her husband is hurt, confused, and frustrated. "Here I am, doing all this work, and she's upset with me." He chases after her, trying to get her to see his side; an argument ensues. Hot words are followed by silence and withdrawal; he doesn't feel appreciated, she doesn't feel heard. How do they work through this?

If this pattern repeats for months, the rift in their marriage expands. Bridging the gap seems impossible.

I grew up in the church, then walked away from God during my teens to my early twenties. During my years as a single man, I threw myself into drugs, alcohol, pornography, promiscuity, adultery, and sex with prostitutes. When I hit twenty-three, God started calling me away from my life of sin. I quit the drugs, alcohol, and promiscuity, but couldn't break away from porn and masturbation.

I met Michelle in 1987; we were married February of 1989. I knew all the right churchy words; she thought I was a great Christian guy. She had no idea she was marrying a porn and sex addict. I abstained from porn and masturbation the first six months of our marriage, but the inevitable stress from putting together two broken people of the opposite sex from two different families with messed-up communication methods started pushing my "medicate with porn" button. Soon I was binging daily.

Lust always leaves a man hungry for more; by the summer of 1991 porn wasn't enough. I had sex with a prostitute during a business trip to Ohio. I was horrified. How could I, the "great Christian guy," have committed adultery two and one-half years after our wedding day? How did I fall so far so fast? The shame and guilt were more than I could take, so I decided to call Michelle and come clean.

I'll never forget that phone call; it still brings tears to my eyes. Michelle was shocked, then started crying, with deep, heavy sobs, the kind that come from a broken heart. She kept repeating, *"Mike, Mike, Mike . . . oh Mike . . ."* It was then that the reality I'd hurt Michelle deeply broke through the fog; this was no "Honey I messed up please forgive me and let's move on" deal. I'd shattered our marriage vows, and had no idea if we would make it.

Thus began the long, fumbling, painful process of healing and restoration. Anger, fighting, misfired communication, confusion, crying, and cold silence laced our marriage for months.

I'm amazed Michelle didn't leave me; biblically, she had every right to. Instead, she showed me grace and kindness that can only be described as amazing by working through the healing process with me.

God did an incredible work in our relationship. Today our bond is strong, as is our commitment to each other. More of our story is provided in my first book, *The Road to Grace: Finding True Freedom from the Bondage of Sexual Addiction*.

Every marriage is of profound importance and value to God. No matter how deep the wounds or what you've been through, the Lord can make something new and wonderful from the wreckage. I've seen him work a miracle in my life and in the lives of others I've been privileged to help. One couple I know who were days away from finalizing their divorce stopped the proceedings at the last minute. Months later they visited me; it was amazing to see the change in their relationship.

> *Marriage is to be held in honor among all, and the marriage bed is to be undefiled; for fornicators and adulterers God will judge.*
>
> Hebrews 13:4

By design, God put the two of you two together; He has a purpose for your marriage. Wives, in spite of the pain and trauma you're experiencing, the Lord didn't make a mistake when he paired you with your lust-ensnared husband. He has a plan for both of you, and He can walk you through the storm if you're both willing to cooperate with the process.

It will not be easy. In the chapters ahead we'll work our way through what may feel like a minefield at times; some issues will be emotionally charged. Several days after I exposed my adultery to Michelle, she found a book I had been reading on sexual addiction that had a list of twenty questions to determine if someone was a sex addict. She asked me every one. I was squirming in shame and embarrassment and wanted to crawl into a hole, but answered each question truthfully. In the end it turned out to be a good move on her part because it opened the door of communication and helped us understand each other.

Open, honest communication on the tough issues is critical. When a wounded couple is in the recovery process, emotions are raw and exposed. Some topics provoke pain, while others can stoke the fire of anger. These places need to be visited, worked through, and resolved to bring resolution and healing. Ostrich holes don't provide healing. If we don't bring these issues to light, the underlying resentment, shame, hurt, and anger will continue to torment your marriage.

So let's move forward. Healing and restoration are possible and there is hope; we serve a God who's in the business of mending broken hearts.

1

SETTING THE STAGE

I suggest you read through this entire workbook together, especially this chapter. It's important that you're both in agreement with the process as we move forward. At the end of each topic there is a section for you to work the assignments, journal your emotions, and/or record decisions that were made. You can use this copy together, or, if you want to keep your notes private you may consider using two copies, one for each spouse.

Let's set the stage.

ASSUMPTIONS

This book is written with the following assumptions:

1. You are both Christians, believe the Bible is the inspired word of God, and have a desire to honor Him with your lives. This is important because the word of God is the standard for this workbook.

2. You're *both* committed to doing whatever it takes to heal your marriage. Some assume that once the husband ceases to sin sexually everything will be okay. The wife has as much work to do to heal as her husband does to break free; you both have a critical role to play. The will to persevere will

play a key role in your recovery as you work through the assignments, examine the issues of the heart, and make adjustments in your relationship.

3. You're in agreement that the only God-ordained context for sex is in marriage between a husband and his wife. Solo acts of masturbation, pornography, sex with anyone outside of marriage, or other forms of sexual sin such as visiting stripper bars, phone sex, or watching R-rated movies with sex scenes are sin. Some may balk at the idea of solo masturbation being a problem; for an in-depth examination of this topic from a Biblical perspective see chapter 6 of my first book, *The Road to Grace: Finding True Freedom from the Bondage of Sexual Addiction,* and chapter 26 of my second book, *100 Days on The Road to Grace.* You can also view the masturbation article on the Blazing Grace website at http://www.blazinggrace.org/masturbation/. It's important that you're both on the same page with this issue; sex is a gift from God and should be reserved for the marriage bed.

4. All disclosures of porn use, adultery, affairs, or other forms of sexual sin have been made. If not, please wait until this is done so you can proceed without getting sidetracked by painful detours.

COMMITMENT TO HONESTY

Lying, hiding, and deceit *always* accompany sexual sin. When the truth comes out, most wives are shocked to discover that the man they married has been lying to them for most, if not all, of their marriage. Trust, the cornerstone of every relationship, is shattered.

If trust is not rebuilt the marriage cannot be restored. Men, *I can't emphasize enough how critically important this is: from this day forward if your wife asks you a question, you must answer her truthfully.* "Truthfully" includes no lies by omission. If she asks you when you last masturbated to porn, tell her. If she wants to know every device you've acted out with (your home PC, smartphone, office computer, etc.), list them.

One of the worst things you can do to sabotage the rebuilding process is keep lying. Don't be fooled into thinking she won't find out; if you're Christian, you're God's son, and He will expose the truth in His time.

> *Do not be deceived, God is not mocked; for whatever a man sows, this he will also reap. For the one who sows to his own flesh will from the flesh reap corruption, but the one who sows to the Spirit will from the Spirit reap eternal life.*
> Galatians 6:7–8

As I described in the last chapter, I know how uncomfortable those questions from a wife can be. Even so, rigorous honesty is the only way to rebuild trust.

Before proceeding to the next chapter, please make a firm commitment to God and your wife that you will stop all lying and deceit from today forward.

TIME

When Michelle and I began the healing process, I wanted to hurry up and get through it so we could "be normal again." What I didn't understand was that our marriage had been razed to the ground. The cornerstone of trust needed to be reset, new communication patterns learned, and faulty ones discarded. Our bond and love needed restoration and invigoration.

This will take time; focus on the journey, not the end result. Don't rush through the topics. Take the course at a pace that works for you without forcing it. Some assignments will be easy, with little time or emotional investment needed. Others might require several days or even weeks to work through. That's okay. It took years to get to where you are today. Now take the time to carefully rebuild your marriage, brick by brick. Think of it as building a house; the investment of time and quality of resources the builder puts into it determines how long the finished product will last. Putting the same effort into your relationship will increase the chances that one day you'll have a new marriage that's so rock–solid that nothing can shake it.

The two of you are not alone. God will be helping, strengthening, encouraging, teaching, and healing you as you walk with Him. This workbook is about receiving His help as much as it is providing you with the process.

Some people beat themselves or their spouses up because they can't heal, move forward, or "fix their marriage" as quickly as they'd like. Statements like "Why can't you just stop acting out" or "Why can't you get over this?" should be set aside. Give yourself and your spouse the time you need to heal and recover.

COMMUNICATION

One of the biggest reasons couples go to marital counseling is they need a safe place to share where they won't get attacked by their spouse. Following is a communication structure you can use that will make it easier to talk freely.

Decide who will start.

The person who shares first begins by expressing their thoughts and feelings about the issue (staying on topic helps— avoid rabbit trails). While they're sharing, the listening spouse is not to speak. All impulses to defend, rebut, or, especially, attack their spouse is to be set aside. *The only goal for the listening spouse is to make their mate feel heard and understood.*

No insults, sarcasm, antagonizing, belittling, attacking, or name-calling are allowed. Your goal is to work *with* your spouse, not against them. You're not in a contest to prove who's right. As hard as it will be, work to keep your emotions in check. Expressing them is good and necessary, but an angry explosion that turns abusive will shut your spouse down. Regardless of your spouse's failures or whether you feel they deserve it, treat them with respect.

Avoiding the word "you" as much as possible will help keep your spouse from going on the defensive. "You've destroyed our marriage and there's no hope because you're a pervert and a liar!" will send your husband into a foxhole. Instead, try to communicate with "I" statements such as "I'm hurting so much that I don't know if I can forgive you; I've got a lot of anger and resentment for the way I've been treated and lied to." Responses like this provide insight to your heart and will hopefully spark compassion from your spouse. It states what they did to you and how it affected you without attacking them.

Once the sharing spouse has finished, the listening spouse is to reflect, or mirror, what the sharing spouse expressed so the sharing spouse knows they were heard and understood. Again, the listening spouse is not to defend, dispute, or take over the conversation. Here's an example: "You're feeling wounded because of how I hurt you with my sexual sin. And it's hard for you to forgive me because there's so much pain and anger. Is this how you feel?"

If the sharing spouse agrees, then the listening spouse can do one of two things:

1. Ask the sharing spouse to expand on their original statement, put forward a question, or comment on what was shared, such as "I feel horrible for what I've done to you and would like to know more about what you're going through," or "Thanks for sharing that with me. Can you tell me what I could do to help you?"

   If the sharing spouse doesn't want to talk more, don't force it. Just opening up and sharing feelings can be a challenge for some topics. A statement from the sharing spouse such this works: "I'm not ready to go there just yet. I need a little time."

2. The listening spouse can proceed to take the floor while the sharing spouse assumes the listening role. Continue the process until both sides feel heard, that they have worked through the issue, and are ready to move on.

Many marriages are made up of one introvert and one extrovert. The extrovert may need to work hard at listening and holding their tongue, while the introvert may need to force him/herself to open up and reveal their inner world. Extroverts tend to talk about themselves, while introverts think about themselves. Both sides need to work at focusing on the other so the marriage can heal. When two people care more about the other than themselves or their agenda, healing can occur. We want the husband genuinely concerned for his wife's healing, just as we want the wife invested in her husband's journey to freedom from sexual sin.

> *Do nothing from selfishness or empty conceit, but with humility of mind regard one another as more important than yourselves; do not merely look out for your own personal interests, but also for the interests of others.*
> *Philippians 2:3–4*

Strive to work together. If you're not both in agreement on an issue, wait until you can find a way to come together on it. Don't force your will on the other. Let God have room to work so He can help you put together the pieces.

Part of being a safe spouse involves honoring your mate's desire for confidentiality. If the wife, for example, wants to tell her mom, who crosses boundaries at will and doesn't know when to back off, but her husband doesn't, honor the husband's request. If the husband wants to tell one of his buddies but his wife isn't ready, don't. Honor your spouse by putting them first; don't make a move unless you're in agreement.

If either side makes a mistake and says something hurtful, apologize immediately, and move on. If the offended party needs time to recover, take a break. Don't demand that the other side bounces back quickly if you hurt them. If you're the offended side, it's to your advantage to forgive as quickly as you're able. Work to keep bitterness away from your marriage as much as possible.

Setting a goal of creating a safe environment will open the doors to heart-level communication and healing.

IF YOU GET STUCK

Every couple has moments when they hit a wall and can't agree on an issue. When this happens, follow these steps:

1. Look at what God's word says about the matter.

2. Remember that the spirit of the law (love) is often more important than the letter (Romans 8, 1 Corinthians 13). It's possible to be technically right but spiritually wrong; this usually happens when one side is trying to dominate their spouse instead of working with them.

3. Discern the essential from nonessential issues. An essential issue would be no porn or adultery; there shouldn't be any negotiation on whether these are permitted. Which day of the week your spouse goes to a support group is a nonessential and not worth taking a hard line on; what's critical is that the person goes.

4.   When you know you need to, let your spouse win. Sometimes winning means letting the other side have their way on a nonessential. Don't be a control freak and insist on what you want all the time.

5.   Examine your motives. Take a hard look at what's going on inside of you. Are you being selfish, proud, or fearful? Are you so hurt, angry, or wrapped up in yourself that you're not listening to what your spouse is saying? If they're pointing out a flaw of yours (or if this book has exposed it), are you putting up a smokescreen to avoid admitting that you have work to do?

6.   Pray. Ask God what He wants you to do, then wait for His answer. Remember that you and your spouse are not alone; divine help is near.

7.   Step back. Sometimes giving an issue time to breathe can clear the way for an answer to present itself.

8.   If, after doing the above, you're still at an impasse and would like outside input, feel free to send me an email. My contact info is at the back of this book.

PRAYER

We need to soak your marriage in prayer.

Pray together once a day, every day, no matter how you feel. There may be instances when one spouse is so upset they can't say a word and the other has to do all the praying. That's okay; whatever it takes. One survey showed that of couples who pray together daily, only one couple in 1,000 will divorce, while of couples who don't pray together one in two will divorce. A cord of three strands is not quickly broken (Ecclesiastes 4:12). Prayer is one of the most important tools of the healing process.

Before you begin a chapter, pray together. Request God's help to diffuse any potentially explosive situations. Pride can pop up at a moment's notice, sparking both sides to take up defensive positions. Ask the Lord for the grace and humility to surrender your rights and the discernment to understand what you're going through. You're in a spiritual battle with an enemy who wants to destroy your marriage; Satan will poke and prod you with all the resentment, discouragement, and confusion he can. He doesn't want your marriage to heal because he knows you'll be a glowing testimony of God's grace.

Read all of the instructions for each action step before you proceed so you have a complete understanding of what you need to do. This is especially important when the topic is emotionally charged.

After completing an assignment, pray again. Ask God to seal what's been resolved and provide the will to take action. If your spouse needs healing in an area, pray for them.

Let's pray now. Pray together, and ask God to rebuild your marriage. Surrender the process and your spouse into His hands. Pray for each other. Ask for the help to focus on listening and caring for your spouse, and for the Lord to shut down all attempts of the enemy to thwart His work of restoring your relationship.

Be of sober spirit, be on the alert. Your adversary, the devil, prowls around like a roaring lion, seeking someone to devour. But resist him, firm in your faith, knowing that the same experiences of suffering are being accomplished by your brethren who are in the world. After you have suffered for a little while, the God of all grace, who called you to His eternal glory in Christ, will Himself perfect, confirm, strengthen and establish you. To Him be dominion forever and ever. Amen.

1 Peter 5:8–11

2

TAKING OWNERSHIP

PRAY

For the purposes of this course, I'll refer to the husband as the one who has committed sexual sin. I'm aware there are marriages where the wife committed adultery. If this is the case merely reverse the roles as described in this book.

Some men blame their wives for their sexual sin; not enough sex, nagging, and fighting are a few of the excuses they fire off. Every attempt by a husband to blame his wife for his sin is a smoke screen to keep him from taking a hard look in the mirror.

My hope is that you're not one of those men. Either way, it's important that we begin with the husband taking complete responsibility for his choices to engage in sexual sin. This is important for two reasons:

1. For the marriage to heal and the man to break free from lust, all justification, blaming, and denial, which have corrupted his character, must stop. These are attempts to hold on to sexual sin; your wife can't trust you while you're playing games with lust. Since God's word says all sex outside of marriage is sin, the husband has no ground to stand on to claim that his wife is responsible for his choices.

Some men might say, "But my wife has been closing me off sexually for a while now. How else am I supposed to find sexual release?" Many wives sensed when their husbands were engaging in sexual sin long before it hit the fan. Even if they didn't know the truth, a wife can read her husband like a book. If I'm messed up or had a hard day, Michelle can take one look at me and know something's wrong. Men who are in bondage to lust are sex and self-absorbed, critical, bitter, and miserable, so after years of being treated poorly it wouldn't be unreasonable for her to shut down sexually. Porn, adultery, and treating your wife harshly are sex-killers for a marriage; get the relationship right and the sex will come later.

2. Your wife needs to hear you take responsibility. Many women report that their husband's sexual sin gutted their self-esteem. Michelle told me I destroyed hers. Some women internalize the lie that they weren't good enough for her husband as a wife, lover, or mother to their children. If they just did (fill in the blank) better, maybe their husband wouldn't have turned to porn or an affair. Unfortunately, there are counselors in and out of the church who stir more confusion and chaos into the pot by saying foolish things like "If you just gave him more sex he wouldn't have this problem." No, it wouldn't. Lust always leaves a man wanting more; it never satisfies. In the early years of our marriage, Michelle and I had a great sex life, even when I was using porn. The truth is that a wife can't fix her husband's lust problem no matter what she does.

    The wife of the husband who's using porn may see herself

fighting an unwinnable war against "the perfect woman." If this is her perception, she'll be trapped in an unending cycle of trying to be "the perfect wife," which only leads to more despair, frustration, and anger. Until her husband takes complete ownership for his sin, the healing process will stay grounded.

On the positive side, a man who takes full responsibility shows his wife he's serious about rebuilding their relationship. By choosing the path of humility, he plants seeds of hope in their marriage garden. Moreover, God *promises* to honor humility with grace (James 4:6); for Christians this is an awesome promise that can yield unexpected blessings.

When a husband takes ownership of his sin, he creates a safe environment his wife can heal in. Instead of shutting her heart down and putting her on the defensive by blaming her, now he gives her a reason to hope. She can stop competing with the "perfect woman" or seeing herself as a failure. She is God's gift to her husband, not the cause of his sin. She has hope because he's not going to play games with lust or hide in denial or justification as many men do. He's saying, "I'm broken; I need help. I want to break free from sexual sin and heal our marriage. I'm sorry I hurt you."

For today's action step, the husband is to take complete ownership for all of his sexual sin. He is to release his wife from all responsibility for all of his choices, no matter what was going on in their marriage.

Husbands, you can write this out in a letter, or verbalize it. Wives, allow him the freedom to express his feelings in the way that is least intimidating to him. He may need a little time to put his thoughts together and work through his emotions.

When the husband has completed his part, the wife is to reflect, or mirror, what her husband said. If he truly took ownership he'll want to know that you heard him.

Then the husband is to invite his wife to share her feelings about his confession. Wives, remember that shame is a debilitating part of sexual sin. Some men are terrified of letting their guard down; your husband may feel like he took a risk today when he exposed his feelings. You want to encourage him to keep taking the steps of humility. If your emotions are raw at the moment and you're feeling overwhelmed, (i.e., if you're afraid that anger might overtake you) you might want to consider saying something like "I appreciate what you've said; I'm in a bad place right now. Please give me a little time to absorb this so I can provide a response that might be better for both of us."

After she shares, the husband is to mirror his wife's comments. Husbands, remember that this is painful for your wife; even something as positive as taking responsibility can rub salt in her wound. No matter what she says, do not defend yourself. *Focus on listening to her and making sure she feels heard.* Allowing her to express her feelings without interruption will help her feel safe with you. You want her to feel free to open up with you with everything she's going through.

In spite of how emotionally charged this action step may be for both of you, remember that your goal is to work *with* each other. Striving to understand your spouse will help open the doors of communication, which is an important part of this process.

CLOSE WITH PRAYER.

3

THE ACTION PLAN

For the husband to break free from sexual sin and restore trust in his marriage, he must take the action steps necessary to eliminate the temptation points of lust under his control. We hear often from wives that their husbands are saying, "Awww, I can do this on my own; I don't need help." That's denial and justification talking; it's also a surefire way to divorce. A man who's spent years saturating his mind with porn and giving in to temptation cannot break free on his own; I know because I tried, and so have many others. The stronghold of lust cannot be broken in isolation, nor, after years of succumbing, will your compromised and weakened character suddenly manifest the strength to say "no" on an ongoing basis.

His wife, who's been traumatized and trying to cope with the pain, anger, and confusion, cannot heal in isolation either. Keeping all of the emotions and expectations for help contained in a marriage puts an enormous amount of pressure on the relationship. There will be many times when you aren't able to receive encouragement or support from your husband because he's the one who hurt you. There will also be days when he's upside down from trying to navigate the road of sexual purity. It's important that you have at least one other woman you can share your journey with.

Today we're going to set an action plan for both of you.

1. Until the husband has at least one year of continuous victory over sexual sin, defined as no masturbation, porn, or sex outside of marriage, he must attend a support group or meet with another man for the purpose of accountability at least once a week. Lust feeds off of isolation; from today forward he can no longer walk as a Christian loner. (I've written extensively about isolation and why it must be avoided in my first two books and on the Blazing Grace website.) There are many ministries and churches with support groups available. We also have forums on the Blazing Grace website. You will still need face-to-face accountability; the forums are a way to get started today.

2. Set a schedule of when the husband will be accountable to his wife with sexual sin; the frequency will depend on what's best for the marriage. Some wives want to meet for accountability more often (such as once a week), others want less (once a month). Discuss a frequency that would be healthy for his recovery and help his wife rebuild trust. I advise against making the wife the husband's daily accountability partner so that the marriage has time to breathe. Once every seven days is sufficient. If you're a wife and are thinking, "I want to know *every* day," please consider the following: Let's say you had a problem with overeating. You've gained 150 pounds, are having health problems, and your husband is pressuring you to change your diet and exercise consistently. It's something you've struggled with for years and are ashamed

of; it's hard for you to talk about it. Would you want your husband checking up on you every day, or would you want a little breathing room?

After their husband's disclosure, many wives understandably struggle with a profound sense of insecurity and fear. When trust is absent in a marriage, fear can rush in and fill the void. The more you give in to fear the stronger it becomes; eventually it can drive you. If fear and insecurity have the wheel of your heart, share this openly with your husband, and/or your support partner. Then look to the Lord. Your faith in Him will release the power to evict fear. It may feel shaky at first, but all it takes is a tiny mustard seed's worth of trust to make a difference.

Then go back and discuss what would be a healthy frequency for accountability in your marriage.

3. The wife is to plan to meet, or at least talk to, another woman on a weekly basis. Having a woman who will support your efforts to heal your marriage can provide encouragement, new perspective, and release from pent-up emotions. A support group of other women is best, but sadly there are far fewer support groups for wives of sex addicts than there are for the sex addicts themselves. If you're not able to locate a support partner, we offer weekly phone groups for wives at Blazing Grace. Send an email to email@blazinggrace.org and we'll get you plugged in.

    I do not recommend making a family member a support partner for the wife. Many family members do more harm than good; some are prone to grudges, judging, backbiting, tearing down your husband, or pressing you to file for divorce. Unless you're 100% sure a family member can be a clean sounding board, avoid them; the last thing you need is Aunty Betty the Battleaxe poisoning your heart with resentment. Your support partner's primary goal should be to point you to Christ and help you cultivate healing for yourself and your marriage.

4. The husband and wife are to set a plan to remove the stumbling blocks of temptation that the husband succumbs to which are under their control. This requires input and maybe some negotiation from both sides; changes will need to be made in the home that will affect the entire family. For example, if Internet porn is the problem, the family computer may need to be relocated to a spot where no one can get on without being seen. Cable TV a problem? It has to go. Wife bringing in *People* magazine or lingerie catalogs like Victoria's Secret with sexually provocative images? Gone.

    While this may sound drastic, if the husband and wife do not make their home a porn and temptation-free zone, the husband will be prone to repeated relapses and may never break free. As an alcoholic has lost all willpower to say no to the temptation to drink, so the porn addict cannot resist the temptation to view porn when it's accessible. Access to porn or R-rated movies with sex scenes in your home is the same as an alcoholic keeping a kegger in the kitchen.

Jesus set the standard for how to deal with besetting sin in Matthew 5:30:

If your right hand makes you stumble, cut it off and throw it from you; for it is better for you to lose one of the parts of your body, than for your whole body to go into hell.

When a man is in bondage to sexual sin, taking no-compromise action is a must. Whatever is taking him down that is under his control must be eliminated. Setting your husband's issues aside, which would be beneficial for your family: more secular media in your home, or less? How many hours do your family members spend immersing themselves in the world's messages and lies? How much time do you spend together as a family just talking and having fun? If you or your children are spending hours playing video games or watching TV, now would be a good time to evaluate your media consumption.

To make your plan, have the husband list every way he has fallen to temptation, including the location. This could be TV, Internet, stripper bars, R-rated movies, magazines, DVDs, smartphones, relationships that have gone too far, hotel porn, or others. You also want to list the places he's fallen such as home, the office, in the car, etc.

Then the two of you need to come up with an action plan to eliminate every temptation point under your control. Take each item and discuss the best way for your family to deal with it. There isn't a one-size-fits-all plan because each man, his trigger points, and his stumbling blocks are different.

My take on the best way to deal with Internet porn is to have software installed on every device that emails a list of every website the husband visited to his wife and his male accountability partner. Porn blocking software should be installed, but you should know that I've never heard of a guy who couldn't get around porn blocking software when he wanted to. The challenge of beating it becomes part of the game of the hunt; if they stay at it long enough they'll eventually beat it.

While porn blocking software can be circumvented, the knowledge that their wife will know they've viewed porn within minutes is enough to put fear into most men. I'll think long and hard about those consequences before clicking on the wrong link.

If there was an affair, the relationship with the other person is to be permanently severed. If you work with that person, look for another job. There must be no further contact.

If the husband travels for business and stumbles with hotel porn, he can call ahead and ask the front desk to turn off all cable movies, set a firm boundary for himself that he is not allowed to turn on the TV for any reason while travelling, and/or call his wife and/or an accountability partner upon check-in and checkout to add an extra level of accountability. If this isn't enough and the husband keeps falling, he may have to stop travelling until he gets his feet on the ground, or find another job.

If, after setting your plan, the husband stumbles again, this is a signal that there's a loophole that needs to be closed. Modify your plan as needed and keep going.

Husbands, make sure you are thorough and completely honest with your temptation points, triggers, and stumbling blocks when making this plan with your wife. There must be no hidden backups, stashes, or devices she doesn't know about; concealing your access points to porn or other forms of sexual sin is lying and deceit. If you're hiding something and your wife finds out later (which, they always do), it will destroy the progress you've made and make it harder for her to trust you.

After the two of you have set your plan and are in 100% agreement, execute! Hold each other accountable to the course you've set, and stick with it. I can almost guarantee you'll encounter resistance from the enemy with thoughts like "Isn't this a little overboard? What will your friends think if you don't watch TV and keep up on the latest shows? You don't really need to cancel the subscription to Victoria's Secret; just hide the magazines when they come in. *This is your husband's problem; why should you have to sacrifice for his mistakes?*"

The action points we discussed today involve radical life change. You may not be able to watch or have the things other Christians think are okay. So what? Your most important goal is pleasing God; going all out for your marriage and making it a bigger priority than consuming junk-media will surely please Him. Jesus told us to count the cost of following Him and take up our cross. Letting go of some of the garbage this world calls entertainment is nothing compared to the peace that comes from a clear conscience.

Do not proceed to the next topic until this step is complete.

PRAY

4

UNDERSTANDING MY SPOUSE

PRAY

One reason couples go to a marital counselor is because neither side feels heard or understood. This can be a big problem in marriage even without the fallout from sexual sin. Understanding what your spouse is going through and caring for them in the process adds a building block to the restoration process.

Today we're going to focus on understanding each other. Begin by deciding which person will share first; the listening spouse is to ask the questions listed below. Before you begin, remember that you both need to create a safe environment to encourage your spouse to share freely; no interrupting, criticizing, or defending. The goal is to make your spouse feel heard and cared for.

The husband is to ask his wife:
"How has my sexual sin impacted you?"
"What are your greatest fears and concerns?"
"How can I help you heal?"
"How can I help you rebuild trust?"

The wife is to ask her husband:
"What is it like being addicted to sexual sin?"
"How has the shame affected you?"
"What are your greatest fears?"
"How can I help you break free?"

Husbands: Your wife may have a hard time understanding why you would hide sexual sin from her. You might share the debilitating effect of shame and/or the fear of rejection. If your wife has shared in the past that she feels your use of porn is her fault because she wasn't (fill in the blank) enough, you can help her understand the addictive power of sexual lust and its grip on you. You also might explain how you felt about it; I know I hated it even while it was driving me. Help her understand how sexual sin has affected your character, your relationship with her, and God.

Wives: Many husbands don't understand the depth of the pain that porn and/or adultery causes their spouse. Most men don't feel as deeply as their wives do; they may not understand why she can't bounce back quickly and why the healing process can take months if not years. Help him understand your heart. Share how discovering his sin has impacted you, including how it's affected your relationships with your husband, your friends, and God. If going out in public is hard for you because you're wondering if he's lusting for other women, tell him.

Here are several tips for your time together:

1. Use the communication structure provided in chapter 1 if needed.

2. Be patient with each other. If you're not getting through, a word picture can bridge the gap. Work to find creative ways to get your point across if needed.

3. Focus on expressing how you feel and what you're going through. Don't cross over and start telling your mate what they should or shouldn't have done, or how they should feel or have responded in a certain situation. The past can't be changed, and you're trying to move forward.

4. Discuss what you've both lost. Grieve together. This will help you connect; release the old marriage so you can rebuild a new one.

Write down what you learned about each other today in the space provided.

PRAY

5

PUTTING THE TWO SIDES TOGETHER

PRAY

Let's return to the vignette from the Introduction.

Husband goes to support group. For what may be the first time in his life, he's beginning to gain traction and experience freedom from sexual sin. Husband comes home excitedly and tells his wife, "I've been sober for ninety days! Check out the recovery coin they gave me!"

Wife breaks down into tears. She snaps at him with a sarcastic bite: "Good for you. My husband the porn addict didn't masturbate to pictures of naked women for several months. Yay."

Her husband, who expected his wife to high-five him, is confused and frustrated. What happened? Minutes ago everyone at his support group was slapping him on the back and telling him what a great guy he was for earning his ninety-day coin. This was a big deal to him because he's *never* gone three months as an adult without using porn. For once in his life he has new hope for the future . . . or at least he thought he did.

For his wife, her husband's announcement triggered her pain and anger all over again. He reminded her that he *hasn't* been faithful to her for the duration of their marriage. For him to be proud of several months of sexual purity is insane to her. Doesn't he get it? She didn't sign up for a marriage with a sex addict and all the pain and trauma that goes with it. He shouldn't need this support group in the first place; his porn buddies are forgetting that his wife is sitting at home among the rubble of a ruined marriage.

The conversation flies downhill from there. He gets angry and frustrated; he may defend himself, apologize for the hundredth time, or, worst case, attack her for "not being supportive." Her response is that he doesn't care about her feelings and has no idea what she's going through.

So how do we bring the two sides together?

Let's start with the support group. Accountability is a vital part of the husband's recovery; he won't make it without it. Some support groups place huge emphasis on length of sexual sobriety and can exalt those who "have it" it to prophet-like status. Husbands can get so caught up in their progress that they forget their marriage is in pieces. If a man is successful by the group's standards but he's treating his wife poorly at home, his recovery is one-sided at best. He's just a jerk who isn't looking at porn for the moment. The "she should appreciate me for what I did" mentality has too much self in it.

This isn't to say that the husband shouldn't desire to share his progress with his wife, or that sexual sobriety or support groups are bad. It comes down to a realignment of his priorities and adjustment of his approach. The key for him is to adopt a position of humility with his wife; her feelings come first, not his victories. Scripture shows us what that looks like:

Do nothing from selfishness or empty conceit, but with humility of mind regard one another as more important than yourselves; do not merely look out for your own personal interests, but also for the interests of others. Have this attitude in yourselves which was also in Christ Jesus, who, although He existed in the form of God, did not regard equality with God a thing to be grasped, but emptied Himself, taking the form of a bond-servant, and being made in the likeness of men. Being found in appearance as a man, He humbled Himself by becoming obedient to the point of death, even death on a cross.

Philippians 2:3–8

Wives can smell pride and self-absorption on their husbands from a mile away. If he charges in the door and the first thing out of his mouth is how great he is because he didn't masturbate for three months, she takes it that he's in Me Mode again. From her viewpoint, he hasn't changed. Sexual sin warps a man into self-obsession. *Husbands, your wives are watching you to see if you're the same self-absorbed man you were before.* They know that sexual sin is all about you; pleasing yourself. For your wife to believe you've turned a corner it will be important that you show her you care more about her than yourself.

Here's a better way for the scenario at the beginning of this chapter to play out.

Husband comes home from support group. He asks his wife how she's doing. She looks at him quizzically and wonders why he's not talking about himself again, and replies, guard-edly, "Okay." He then responds with a question such as "What would you like to do now?" or "Is there anything you'd like to talk about?" or "How was your day?" By focusing on her first, he's showing her that he cares about her, and she's a bigger priority to him than his recovery.

If she opens up, the smartest thing he can do is employ re-flective listening, making sure she feels heard, without defending, reacting rashly, or interrupting. If she doesn't want to talk at the moment, he lets it go, and they move on.

As for his ninety-day coin, he waits until she asks how he's doing or what happened at the group before sharing with her. If it takes awhile for her to ask, it's okay; she's his biggest priority. The Bible calls it dying to self.

Wives, if your husband adopts a position of humility and asks you to share your feelings, work with him. Your marriage is not going to heal if you don't communicate; help him understand where you are. Tell him what you need, even if it's just for him to listen or take out the trash. Men are horrible mind-readers and cue-takers; we need black-and-white instructions. Your husband may be dying to know how to help you, but feel powerless or afraid of saying the wrong thing. If you've had a miserable day with screaming kids and need your husband to take the kids for the next hour so you can have a "Calgon take me away" mo-ment in the bathtub, tell him.

The wife's emotions will be volatile for a while; what she needs today won't be the same tomorrow. Husbands, don't make a set "how I am going to fix my wife" recovery plan—especially one based on how she reacted in the past. Your goal should be to walk with her one day at a time, and minister and care for her in the way that she needs in the moment. Be flexible and work with each other.

The rebuilding process includes getting the two of you to work with, instead of against, each other. Achieving this can make a hard road a little less difficult. Working together doesn't look the same for every marriage; find what works for the two of you.

Discuss what you've learned today and what you will change moving forward.

PRAY

6

PRIORITIES

PRAY

Today we're going to look at the priority marriage should be to a husband and wife.

In Ephesians 5:22, Paul calls wives to be subject to their husbands, *as to the Lord.* In verses 23–24, he writes that wives are to be subject to their husbands in *everything.* There is no other person in Scripture who God has called a married woman to give herself to so freely and completely other than her husband.

In verse 25, Paul commands husbands to love their wives with a love so intense that it mirrors Christ's love for the church, who He died for. Verse 29 goes deeper: "No one ever hated his own flesh, but nourishes and cherishes it, just as Christ also does the church." The only person a husband is commanded to "die for, nourish, and cherish" is his wife.

Genesis 2:24 states: "For this reason a man shall leave his father and his mother, and be joined to his wife; and they shall become one flesh." Jesus commented on this verse when He said, "So they are no longer two, but one flesh. What therefore God has joined together, let no man separate" (Matthew 19:6). When a man and woman are married, their relationship supersedes all others, including that of both spouse's parents. Every other human relationship takes second place, even the children.

I hear a lot of Christians say their priorities are God first, spouse second, children third, and then others. Nice words, but it's their actions, the time and energy they put into their marriage, and how they treat their spouse that reveal the truth.

In the early years of my marriage, my actions didn't line up with my words. I was a driven, type-A workaholic and a self-absorbed sex addict; my true priorities were me, career, and sexual sin; God and my wife got the leftovers. I was arrogant and prone to making unilateral decisions for our family, which led to friction and resentment with Michelle.

In 1997 our second son died five days after he was born; God used that event to break me of my habit of making business the main thing. My family suddenly became immensely more important than the office ever would be. For a while.

God set me free from sexual addiction in 1999. I started a support group for sex addicts in 2000, then got Blazing Grace going in 2004. As the ministry grew I got addicted to the toxic rush of it, until I pushed too hard, burned out, and the Lord removed me from ministry from 2008 to 2011. During those four years, God convicted me deeply about my sin of putting ministry above my relationships with Him and Michelle. I had to face my pride; He taught me a lot about humility, obedience, and wisdom during those years. He realigned my priorities once and for all that He comes first, my wife is second, then the rest. Ministry doesn't even make the top four (being a father is third; providing for my family is fourth).

THE ROAD TO GRACE FOR COUPLES

Today, I discuss every major decision for my family, job, and ministry with Michelle before moving forward. If she's not on board, I back off. My wife and I are one flesh and I don't want anything to come between us again—especially work or ministry.

We receive emails from hurting wives whose Christian husbands are in ministry and in bondage to sexual sin. Most of the time, my advice to such men is to get out of ministry for a while and get their relationships with God and their wife right. Every day you continue on the road of messed-up priorities you're closer to a divine spanking; I can tell you from experience that when God disciplines (Hebrews 12:6 calls it scourging) the pain is excruciating. He doesn't do second place with his children.

While men can get caught up in work, ministry, or hobbies, women may make other relationships a bigger priority than their husband. Women may put work or ministry over their husbands too, but the complaints I hear most from men is that their wife's relationships outside of their marriage are a bigger priority. For example, if his wife's parents tell her they think she should take a direction that's opposed to what he prefers, she needs to go with her husband. Although he will make mistakes, God has commanded her to "leave her parents and become one with her husband." He comes first.

She must also give her relationship with her husband greater priority than that of their children. I have four children and know the investment in time and energy a mother must give her children. However, some women immerse their entire identity in being "Mom" and sideline the role of wife. She must be intentional in insuring that he gets more from her than the leftovers of her love, attention, and care.

44

Today's exercise involves examining the priorities of the husband and wife as perceived by their spouse, and working together to make any adjustments necessary.

Each spouse is to go through the list below, and make a mark next to any person or thing they believe their spouse values more than them. We're doing it this way because we have blind spots; we can get so wrapped up in something (like ministry, work, family, other relationships, or hobbies) that we don't realize we're shortchanging our spouse, either because we were raised to do so by our parents, or we've allowed circumstances to go too far.

After both sides have marked their issues, proceed as follows:

Let's say the wife will go first. Her husband has marked that he feels her parents are a higher priority than he is. She is not to become defensive. Instead, she will start by asking these questions:

1. How long have you felt like this?

2. To help me understand, can you please give me some specific examples where I valued my parents more than you?

3. What do I need to do so that you feel I place a higher priority on our relationship than on my parents?

His wife is to focus on listening and understanding her husband's point of view. She is not to debate him or try to talk him out of his perception or feelings; her role is to work *with* him so they can resolve the issue. In some situations it might be as simple as the wife providing clarification over what happened in a specific situation. In others, a shift in priorities coupled with action steps may be needed.

If the wife proposes a solution but the husband doesn't think that will resolve it, they need to continue to negotiate until they work it out. Both sides may need to compromise—if the husband demands that his wife cut off all contact with her parents, for example, this isn't happening (unless they're abusive to her).

Once the first issue has been resolved, keep going until you've worked through every item both sides have marked. Make notes on the adjustments you will make. If there's a long list to work through, you might consider taking it in several bite-sized chunks, spread out over several days.

	Wife	Husband
Parents (His or Hers)	____	____
Children	____	____
Friends	____	____
Work/career	____	____
Ministry	____	____
Sexual sin/porn	____	____
Sports	____	____
Other relationships	____	____
Other sins	____	____
Other hobby	____	____
Other hobby	____	____
Entertainment	____	____
Social media	____	____
Computers	____	____

Other

_____   ____   ____

_____   ____   ____

_____   ____   ____

_____   ____   ____

_____   ____   ____

_____   ____   ____

_____   ____   ____

_____   ____   ____

_____   ____   ____

PRAY

7

WHO'S THE ENEMY?

Begin by praying and asking God to remove any distractions and thoughts from the enemy. You'll see why in a moment.

Every marriage is in a spiritual battle. Satan has his guns pointed at both of you, and will do everything in his power to tear your relationship apart, rupture your family, and wound your children with the effects of divorce.

Here are some of his methods:

1. Seducing and enslaving the husband to sexual sin.

2. Attacking the husband with thoughts such as "There's no hope I can break free," "If others really knew me they couldn't accept or love me," "I dare not tell my wife; if I do she'll divorce me," "Lust is my only source of comfort and love," and "There's no one I can talk to," among others. His goal is to keep the husband stuck in lust, fear, shame, self-absorption, hopelessness, and resentment.

3. He goes after the wife with "If I would have only (fill the in blank) he wouldn't use porn," "I wasn't enough for him," "I

can't compete with the women in those pictures," "My husband doesn't want to break free from sexual sin; maybe he never will," along with the fear of divorce and a future as a single mother. He does everything he can to keep the wife bound in anger, hurt, discouragement, fear, and suspicion.

4. He wants to keep you fighting your spouse. He tries to convince the husband that his wife is against him, rejects him, and is his enemy. He tries to convince the wife that her husband loves porn more than her, there is no hope, and her husband is an enemy who can never be trusted.

Let's set the record straight.

Satan is your enemy. *Your spouse is not your enemy.* They may be blinded by pride, lust, fear, bitterness, discouragement, or struggling to cope with old wounds, and they have the same fallen flesh you do, but your spouse is not your enemy.

> *For our struggle is not against flesh and blood, but*
> *against the rulers, against the powers, against the*
> *world forces of this darkness, against the spiritual*
> *forces of wickedness in the heavenly places.*
>
> *Ephesians 6:12*

God is infinitely more powerful than Satan; He's given you all the tools you need to persevere, heal your marriage, and overcome, which include prayer, His word, interceding friends, faith, the body of Christ, and the power of the Holy Spirit. The keys to accessing and using these tools are humility, brokenness, repentance, obedience to God and His word, and love.

You are not alone. The Creator of the Universe is near, and He *wants* your marriage and family to heal, succeed, and flourish. You're not the only one walking this path, and you have abundant hope because God is in the business of resurrection, setting captives free, and making something wonderful from our sin and sorrow (Romans 8:28).

Some of your biggest battles will be against your own weaknesses; releasing pride and choosing humility, doing what God says even when everything inside of you says no, praying when you don't feel like it, forgiving when you would rather hold onto bitterness, pressing through instead of withdrawing or quitting.

With God's help, you can overcome the enemy and the battles with your flesh. Your marriage can heal. There is a way through. It's not hopeless. It may feel hard today, but if you're willing to continue in the healing process that God has for your marriage, the breakthroughs will come.

Today, with the help of the Holy Spirit, we're going to take some ground back. You'll need a quiet room where you can pray alone with your spouse for 15 to 30 minutes. Both of you are to pray silently and ask the Lord to bring to your minds all the lies of the enemy you've bought into about yourself and your spouse. As the Lord brings them to light, confess the lie out loud, saying something such as, "God, I confess I haven't believed I can break free from sexual sin . . . that you're able to heal my marriage . . . help me forgive . . . or there's hope."

Then announce the truth out loud with something like: "Lord,

You've said that nothing is impossible for You; we believe You want to heal our marriage. Please cement the truth in our hearts now. Please give us the mustard seed of faith we need to trust You to carry us through."

As long as the Holy Spirit keeps exposing lies you've bought into, keep going. Finish by praying for each other and asking God to help you fight together as one against your true enemy. Ask Him to help you to stand firm against every lie, and for the awareness and discernment of the enemy's attacks when they hit.

This doesn't mean all of what you're going through is spiritual, but you need to be discerning and equipped to deal with spiritual attacks when they come.

Keep praying for each other every day; prayer is an effective, powerful, weapon in the battle. You might also consider praying Scripture for your spouse; the Bible calls the Word of God the sword of the Spirit. When you're attacked with fear, shame, the lies of the enemy, or the temptation to attack your spouse, remember what Scripture says about your situation, stand on the truth, and refuse to back down.

8

IF HE FALLS AGAIN

PRAY

This is a chapter I hope you don't need. I hope the husband is going all out to break free from sexual sin, and is taking the action steps we've discussed. But from years of my own experience and the stories of others, I know relapses happen. If a man has spent ten or twenty years or more masturbating to pornography, the possibility of a slip is real.

How a wife might respond will vary depending on the circumstance. If her husband had sex with a person outside of their marriage after an initial disclosure of infidelity, the consequences should be severe: she should consider immediate separation. There are different degrees of separation: her husband can sleep in another room in your house, or he can move out. The separation should continue for at least six months after he has permanently severed the adulterous relationship to show proof there's no going back and he's committed to rebuilding the marriage. Anything less is for the wife to allow her husband to abuse her emotionally and treat her like a prostitute.

If he had sex with a prostitute, there are other issues to consider. Normally no emotional connection or bond was established so there's no relationship to sever. There should be concern he might have contracted a sexually transmitted disease; he should be tested before you resume sexual relations (although your desire for sex with him will probably be quenched for a while). If he's had sex with prostitutes in the past I would suggest separation. If this is the first time he's had sex with a prostitute and he's throwing himself into the recovery process, you might pray for wisdom and seek counsel before considering separation, only because there wasn't an emotional bond created. I don't say this to minimize the act in any way; it took my wife years to recover and heal from my adultery with a prostitute so in no way am I saying it's less of a sin or not painful for you, only that it might be easier for him to cease having sex with prostitutes than it would be to break off an affair. Separation is still a valid option, even if he had sex with a prostitute once.

I used porn in the first year of my marriage and then had sex with a prostitute once prior to my initial disclosure. Michelle didn't ask me to sleep in another room, and I hit the ground running trying to get help.

However, I did fall with porn again, multiple times. I was porn-free for 18 months after my initial disclosure to Michelle, then acted out with it once. I was free for three years after that, then used porn off and on for the next three years. My wife didn't ask me to sleep in another room during this time, largely in part because she told me that the pain from my adultery with having sex with the prostitute was so traumatic that to her what I was doing with porn, although it still hurt, was smaller in comparison.

This isn't to minimize porn use. Today 56% of divorces involve a spouse who is obsessed with pornography; porn alone is enough to destroy a marriage.

For the wife whose husband has fallen with porn again, my advice would be this:

1. Take into consideration the total picture: has he been going to groups, made an action plan, made an effort to work with you, and been improving how he treats you? (Is he working this workbook with you?) Has he shown you by his actions that he's serious about breaking free from porn addiction? Has he been making baby steps of progress? Has his attitude changed? Did he take ownership of his sin, or did he blame, defend, or justify?

    If most of the answers above are yes, you have reason to hope and show him grace and forgiveness. That doesn't mean his actions won't hurt you. He needs to understand the damage porn does to your heart; every use of porn is adultery and he cannot justify it. Be sure to express your feelings to him. Grace and forgiveness are never a license to wound our spouse repeatedly.

2. Review any gaps in the husband's action plan that should be closed. He needs to be accountable to you for making any needed adjustments.

3. Ask him to share what he was going through emotionally when he acted out. Was he stressed, fearful, or lonely? Did he use porn to medicate his feelings? Discuss better coping mechanisms for the next time those challenges come up. Help him to learn from the mistake.

If your husband has not been going to groups, counseling, and/or seeing an accountability partner, if he hasn't taken firm action to remove the stumbling blocks of temptation, if all he's been doing is talking about changing, and especially if he's blaming, defending or justifying, then the outcome needs to be that he's sleeping in another room or moving out until he shows you by consistent actions that he's not playing games.

Several last points:

1. Wives, the counsel I've given here are guidelines for you to consider that I believe are appropriate. You should always pray and ask the Lord what He wants you to do. Wait for the answer, and He will make your path clear; He knows better than anyone how to heal your marriage.

2. Some men are in such a deep lust-stupor that the only thing that will get through are severe consequences. Other men want to do everything they can to recover and they're still learning how to overcome a sin that has held them in bondage for decades. Wives, you know which one of these your husband is; take into consideration what he did, who he is, and where he is in the recovery process.

3. Husbands, if you fall, the best thing you can do is humble yourself, be honest, and refuse to blame or defend yourself. Do not read these consequences I've listed above and think, "Then I won't tell her anything"; you will risk driving yourself further into isolation and sexual sin and put a bigger wedge

between you and your wife. She will catch you eventually, and your relationship will continue its downward spiral.

My hope is you won't need this chapter and it'll only serve as motivation for the husband to keep moving as far away from lust as he can, as fast as he can.

9

REBUILDING TRUST

PRAY

"How can I learn to trust my husband again?"

I hear this question often from wives. The answer: You will slowly rebuild trust as your husband earns it over an extended period of time by treating you with kindness, staying free from sexual sin, and taking consistent action steps.

Forgiveness and trust are two different issues. While every Christian is commanded by God to forgive all who have hurt them (Matthew 6:14–15), the injured wife is not obligated to trust her husband with her heart again; he needs to give her a reason to trust by his actions. To trust is to expose the heart; when a wife doesn't trust her husband what she's really saying is "I have to protect my heart until you can prove to me I won't get hurt again."

Here are ways to rebuild trust:

- Have accountability software email the wife a list of every website the husband visits, from every device he uses.

- Give your wife the passwords to all media devices; TV, computers, etc.

- Tell your wife you will have your accountability partner call her if you slip, and email them both so everyone is on board.

- Keep taking the action steps of going to support groups and counseling. Make meeting with at least one other man for the purpose of accountability a permanent part of your life.

- Care for her and treat her with kindness. If you have been critical, judging, manipulative, and/or blamed her for things you shouldn't have, take ownership, and stop.

- Make her the biggest priority in your life, second only to God, then show her by the way you treat her that she is.

- Never lie again.

- If you say or do something you shouldn't (which happens in every marriage), apologize immediately.

- Resolve the core wounds and/or distorted beliefs in your heart that are driving you to use lust as a Band-Aid.

- Become the servant-leader of your home.

- Have fun with her.

- Cease all sexual acting out.

All of the above are proof of a changed life that will encourage your wife to trust you again.

It takes months, even years, to fully rebuild trust in a marriage. Husbands, don't expect that you'll be able to do one or two nice things for your wife and then everything will be "back to normal." The "old normal" is long gone and you need to make the effort and put in the time it will take to show your wife she can trust you with her heart. Every woman is different, as are the circumstances, which means there isn't a rule for how long it will take her to heal.

Today, ask each other the following questions:

1. "On a scale of one to ten, ten being best, rate your level of trust in me."

2. "Please tell me what I need to do so I can increase your trust in me to as close to a ten as possible."

If you have a list of action items to work on from your spouse's response to the second question, makes notes below. Then follow through.

PRAY

10

NO CONTROL FREAKS ALLOWED

PRAY

The recovery process can feel like standing on a beach ball and juggling several bowling pins. The husband must fight the battle to break free from a life-long addiction to lust, rebuild his character, learn new coping skills, release shame, face his heart and emotions, and work at his marriage. Meanwhile his wife must find a way to heal from the trauma, trust again, rebuild her shattered self-esteem, reorient her relationship with the God who gave her a sex addict for a husband, forgive, and work on the marriage. Oh, and there's the kids too.

With so much turmoil in the mix, it's easy for boundaries to get crossed and one side to attempt to fix or control the other. If this happens the marriage gets messy; when either side digs in to prevent the other from controlling them, the rebuilding process is halted.

A husband or wife who has been abused or had boundaries violated in the past, either by their spouse or another, will bristle at their partner's efforts to control them; incursions into their space are an act of war. Wives may get so wrapped around fear and insecurity that they attempt to control and micromanage their husband's recovery process. The man may respond by withdrawing into his "safe zone" of isolation, which leads to hiding, lies, and the risk of another fall into sexual sin.

The husband cannot force his wife to heal, just as his wife cannot force her husband to go to a support group or counseling. *Each side must give the other the freedom to discover and utilize the tools and methods that will work best for them.*

This can spark fear in both sides. The wife who's twisted in fear spends her days wringing her hands, worrying whether her husband is binging on porn. She's powerless over what he does, which means anything could happen. He might act out, lie, hurt her, they could lose their marriage, or . . .

Then there's the husband. What if his wife never forgives him and stays stuck in pain and bitterness? What if she doesn't open up with another woman and keeps her emotional volcano bottled up, building up pressure for an eruption? What if, just as he's gaining traction in the battle to break free from lust, she says she's had enough and wants a divorce?

It's okay for a wife to demand and expect that her husband gets help, but she must give him the space to work out the recovery process on his own. The husband should encourage his wife to open up with others, but he can't force her to reach out.

The idea of not being in control will send some people (i.e., control freaks) over the edge. Not being able to control others upends the apple cart of their way of life. Some who struggle the most with surrender were hurt in the past; their way of protecting themselves was to make an internal vow that they would never be in a position where they were out of control again. Some have big-time pride issues; the idea of their mate not bowing down and doing what they say enrages them.

For some, the trauma that's inflicted on a marriage from sexual sin has exposed and exacerbated the pain from an old wound; the fear/anger response has come raging out of nowhere and transformed them into a Control Freak.

Maintaining proper boundaries in marriage is a serious issue; you need wisdom and guidance from God to avoid the land mines of "fix and control" so you're not crossing boundaries and messing each other up. Here are some guide posts to provide light for the journey:

Accountability and control are two different things. Your spouse should be accountable to you for their progress, but where you cross the line into Control Freak Territory is when you start telling them what, when, and how. Express your expectation for them to make changes, then give them the freedom to act.

If your spouse attempts to micromanage you, gently remind them you need the space and time to work things out on your own.

Husbands, this isn't an excuse to delay going to a support group, counseling, or doing what you know you need to do. If you're procrastinating or playing games, your wife has every right to demand that you get off your butt.

The best way to diffuse your spouse's impulses to control you and relieve their fear is with your own consistent action in the recovery process. Both sides must do the work; one can't sit on the sidelines.

Ask God to give you the awareness to discern when you're being tempted or are heading into pride/fear/anger/control mode. The Holy Spirit can give your heart a gentle tug that can keep you from going too far.

If you cross into Control Freak Territory, choose humility, confess it to your spouse, and use the experience as a learning tool for the future.

Above all, release the control of your spouse to God. Let the Lord be God in your spouse's life; He is the one who fixes and heals, not you. He does a much better job of changing others than we do. He convicts gently, at the perfect time, and knows the best circumstances to use. When you surrender your spouse to the Lord, you honor Him by inviting Him into your marriage, while putting yourself in a place of humility, trust, and rest. That's a wonderful, refreshing place to be.

Ask your spouse the following questions:

1. Do I have a problem with control?

2. (If the answer is yes) What does that look like? (Anger, fear, manipulation, guilt trips) Can you please give me some specific examples of when I tried to control you?

3. Why do you think I struggle in this area?

If control is an issue for you, share any past wounds or faulty habits you might have developed over the years that contributed to where you are today. Often, our family of origin taught us to be controlling, and now we have to unlearn their mistakes.

Finish your time in prayer with both of you surrendering each other to God. Confess any sins that might have come up today, including fear, which is the opposite of faith.

11

HIS WOUNDS / HER WOUNDS

PRAY

The Little Girl loves her Daddy with everything she has. But he's distracted with work and other things. He rarely hugs her, or expresses love to her. Most of what she hears is criticism; he rarely encourages her. She grows up starved for her father's affection and approval.

The Little Girl grows into a beautiful young woman. She marries a man, who she thinks, is nothing like her father. Their marriage is okay at first . . . sort of . . . but as the years go by he becomes aloof; withdrawn, and critical. One day she walks in on him as he's masturbating to pornography. Her world unravels; deep-seeded anger and hurt well up with such force that she's overwhelmed.

Like many men who are in bondage to lust, her husband has a hard time with intimacy and showing affection. Just like her father.

She tries to forgive her husband, even says the words, but she can't shake the anger and hurt. She bounces between anger and depression; she feels like she's been carrying an emotional burden all of her life, and doesn't know what to do with it.

The Little Boy had a happy, rambunctious childhood. His

parents are loving and kind; everything was going okay . . . until one day, he spends the night at a neighbor's house and one of the boys sexually molests him. Afterwards, his abuser says, "If you ever tell someone what happened I'll do it again." Stunned and fearful, the Little Boy keeps what happened a secret. He feels sick inside; soiled, worthless. He internalizes the lie that what happened was his fault; he's a sick pervert, a freak. Others might condemn him if they knew, so he dare not expose it.

When adolescence hits, the Little Boy discovers masturbation and porn. It gives him a feeling of comfort, and he feels safe, even accepted . . . until the act is over, and then the shame hits.

The Little Boy grows into a handsome young man and meets the Little Girl. She makes him feel alive, and he immediately falls in love. For a while she makes him forget about the emptiness and pain. Maybe all that is resolved . . . he even stops the porn and masturbation.

They get married, and not long after the inevitable friction arises that occurs in every marriage of two broken people. He responds by withdrawing from his wife. She is confused and frustrated, and presses him for answers. The old tapes of unworthiness and shame kick in again, and it's not long before he's hiding in the "safe haven" of porn and masturbation.

They have children, and his wife gains a few pounds. He starts criticizing her; he can evade his inner misery a little when he's "helping her" with her faults. One day, God exposes his sin: his wife walks in on him as he's masturbating to porn, and their marriage blows up. He's overwhelmed with the sense of being an utter failure, and cries out to God for help.

When a husband and wife begin the recovery process from

sexual sin, the wounds from their hearts will be exposed. *If you want complete, deep healing in your marriage so you can forgive from the heart, accept your spouse as they are, and love them freely, you must resolve the core, root issues in both of your hearts. Otherwise, the best you can hope for is superficial, short-lived recovery, and your marriage will continue to flounder.*

I was molested in my teenage years by a female adult who was a trusted relative. Many don't understand the crippling, traumatic, and life-altering effects of sexual abuse. I was terrified of women; intimacy scared me to death. Even though I worshipped them in lust, I also struggled with anger toward them. I had a miserable time trusting others; if they did anything that felt like it was anywhere close to crossing a personal boundary it would trigger my hot button of anger. I also struggled with a profound sense of low self-worth, and felt soiled, ashamed, and at times even disgusted with who I was. I was close to suicide several times in my teen years; at one point I was holding a gun, but couldn't muster the courage to use it on myself.

You can imagine what this meant for my marriage with Michelle. Without understanding what I was doing, I had become a "don't you dare cross my boundaries" control freak. When she would unknowingly do something that would press one of my hot buttons (which, I had many), it would trigger anger, withdrawal, confusion, or depression. It wasn't until I faced my wounds and healed that I was able to find peace and smooth out the rough spots in our marriage I'd been unwittingly creating.

I dread to think of what my marriage would look like today if I had allowed the poison to fester unchecked in my heart. It was eighteen years after the abuse occurred before I dealt with it. Today I would probably be driven by hatred and prone to severe bouts of depression if I hadn't healed. I doubt whether my marriage would have made it.

Please don't get the idea that this is only for those who have been sexually abused. I'm giving you an extreme example from my past to show how unresolved heart issues can upend your marriage. A passive father can damage his kid's heart; when he neglects his children they can internalize the lie that "no one cares about me; I'm not worth loving." Once a lie has set into the core beliefs of the heart, they will drive the man or woman to find a way to silence or avoid the pain by any means possible. This is why many turn to false coping mechanisms like sexual sin, drugs, alcohol, work obsession, stuffing emotions, blaming, criticism, or gluttony.

Distorted heart beliefs wall off the heart from receiving the grace, love, and forgiveness of God, as well as the love of others such as the spouse. If you believe you're too worthless for God to love, the lie will intercept the truth long before it reaches your heart. This is why Bible knowledge isn't enough to walk out the Christian life in victory and love.

Scripture reveals a God who wants to heal you:

The sacrifices of God are a broken spirit; a broken and a contrite heart, O God, You will not despise.
Psalms 51:17

I have seen his ways, but I will heal him; I will lead him and restore comfort to him and to his mourners . . .
Isaiah 57:18

Let's look at the steps that will move you toward healing.

1. Ask God to expose your heart. Confess any fear about facing the wounds, and ask for the grace to press through.

2. Ask your spouse what they see in you and/or know from your past that might need to be resolved. No one knows us like our spouse; they might have told you before but you didn't want to hear it.

3. Once the Lord exposes a damaged area in your heart, ask your spouse to pray for you. If you haven't already, share what happened with them.

4. Find someone you can process your heart with on an ongoing basis. This could be your spouse, a friend, counselor, or pastor. You need someone who is a clean sounding board who can provide new perspective. For example, many who were abused report feeling responsible for what happened; children who lost a parent from divorce struggle with this too. A wise friend can help you see the truth and expose the lies that have weighed you down. They can also help you discard some of the defective coping mechanisms you've turned to. I was constantly on hair trigger alert for any who might "cross my boundaries." A friend helped me see that my hyper vigilant, control-freak ways were destructive to me and those around me. I was always tense, wound up in fear, and ready to burst (or come apart) at a moment's notice. Not

a good way to live life. Most people couldn't tell because I was adept at playing the Christian game . . . except at home.

5. Ask God to open your eyes to all of the lies you bought into about yourself, others, and God. For example, a girl or boy who grows up with an angry, harsh, critical father who is always pointing out their mistakes but never loving or encouraging them can bite hard on lies like these:

a. I am not worthy of love.

b. I am a failure who can never get it right.

c. I need to work harder to be loved.

d. I'm stupid and incompetent like my father said I was.

e. No one cares about or loves me.

f. I must not expose my feelings to other people; if I do I will get hurt.

g. Stuffing my emotions is the only way I can survive.

A person who allows all that emotional and spiritual sewage to run amok in their heart will find themselves looking for comfort and love in the wrong places. They will struggle with receiving love and sincere complements and find it hard to believe in and accept the grace of God. They'll avoid intimacy with their spouse.

Exposing the lies you've bought into is a critical step. Write them down, and highlight or put an asterisk next to the one you believe defines you the most.

6. *For the weapons of our warfare are not of the flesh, but divinely powerful for the destruction of fortresses. We are destroying speculations and every lofty thing raised up against the knowledge of God, and we are taking every thought captive to the obedience of Christ . . .*

2 Corinthians 10:4

So Jesus was saying to those Jews who had believed Him, "If you continue in My word, then you are truly disciples of Mine; and you will know the truth, and the truth will make you free."

John 8:31–32

Now we're going to take some of that territory in your heart back from the enemy.

Take each lie, and ask God to lead you to the truth in His word that will dissolve it. You can do this alone, with your spouse, or a friend. Then, confess each lie as sin, renounce it, and ask God to break the stronghold in your heart and replace it with the truth. Read any verse(s) God has given you to counteract and replace the lies and proclaim them as truth.

For an example, let's take "I am not worthy of love . . .":

"Father in Heaven, I've believed a lie for all of my life that I'm not worthy of love. While Your word says that "there is 'none righteous' (Romans 3:10) and I cannot earn or deserve Your love, in Ephesians 2 You say: *'But God, being rich in mercy, because of His great love with which He loved us, even when we were dead in our transgressions, made us alive together with Christ (by grace you have been saved), and raised us up with Him, and seated us with Him in the heavenly places in Christ Jesus, so that in the ages to come He might show the surpassing riches of His grace in kindness toward us in Christ Jesus. For by grace you have been saved through faith; and that not of yourselves, it is the gift of God; not as a result of works, so that no one may boast. For we are His workmanship, created in Christ Jesus for good works, which God prepared beforehand so that we would walk in them.'*

"In the name of Jesus, as His son/daughter, I reject the lie that I am not worthy of love and can't receive it.

"Lord, I confess that receiving your love is difficult for me. In spite of this, thank you that you do. Please fill my heart to overflowing with the truth. Take every inch of my heart that was controlled with the lie, break the stronghold, and replace it with Your love and peace. Thank you for doing this."

Once you've prayed through every lie, have a friend intercede for your healing as is shown in James 5:16:

Therefore, confess your sins to one another, and pray for one another so that you may be healed. The effective prayer of a righteous man can accomplish much.

You may feel awkward doing this; don't focus on your emotions or trying to "feel healed." You're interrupting a lifelong pattern that has been set in your heart for years, and are in new territory. This is a great place to be.

7. Live in the truth. God is my comfort and protection; what happened before will not happen again. I'm able to defend myself if needed, and am not the fearful, confused kid I was as a teenager. Thus, I can let my guard down. I need to remember that my wife is not the person who molested me, and separate the two. I know I can trust Michelle with my heart, that she loves me, and wants what's best for me. I don't need to trust others with my emotions unless I choose to.

8. Healing is a process that takes time. It's important that you soak in God's word every day. You're used to thinking, feeling, and believing in a different way than you are now, and it's critical that you ground your heart in the truth. Reject the old tapes if they start looping. The enemy will come at you, but stand firm. In time it will get easier and be like brushing off a gnat.

9. Allow yourself to grieve what was lost . . . childhood, innocence, joy, love, time, or relationships that never were what they could have been. Grieving will help you release the past and all the baggage that comes with it.

10. You and your spouse may consider praying the following Scripture for each other:

    *I bow my knees before the Father, from whom every
    family in heaven and on earth derives its name, that
    He would grant you, according to the riches of His
    glory, to be strengthened with power through His*

Spirit in the inner man, so that Christ may dwell in your hearts through faith; and that you, being rooted and grounded in love, may be able to comprehend with all the saints what is the breadth and length and height and depth, and to know the love of Christ which surpasses knowledge, that you may be filled up to all the fullness of God. Now to Him who is able to do far more abundantly beyond all that we ask or think, according to the power that works within us, to Him be the glory in the church and in Christ Jesus to all generations forever and ever. Amen.

Ephesians 3:14–21

11. Forgive.

After eighteen years of being weighed down and tormented with anger and hurt, I was advised by a counselor to write the person who'd molested me a letter stating what they did, and then forgive them. It was a hard letter to write, but as soon as I mailed it I was free. There was a sense of peace; how they responded didn't matter.

When they wrote back, they asked, "Did writing that letter make you feel better?" There was no apology, or acknowledgement of what happened. I didn't care. The long-sought-after peace I finally possessed was worth more than 10 billion apologies.

Whenever you stand praying, forgive, if you have anything against anyone, so that your Father who is in heaven will also forgive you your transgressions.

Mark 11:25

Jesus tells us to forgive without restoration or being asked for it. That's hard. He did it on the cross when He asked God the Father to forgive those who put Him to death. If you wait for the person who hurt you to come and ask for forgiveness, it may never happen. The same goes if you wait until you feel like forgiving them: forgiveness is an act of the will, not the emotions. Our feelings that can keep us from forgiving.

Much of what keeps us from forgiving is pride; we want them to pay. Or at least sweat it out a little. You may need to ask God for the humility and grace to forgive those who have hurt you the most.

That's a prayer I believe He would answer.

PRAY

12

WEAVING HUMILITY AND GRACE INTO THE MARRIAGE

But He gives a greater grace. Therefore it says, "God is opposed to the proud, but gives grace to the humble. Submit therefore to God."
James 4:6–7

. . . and all of you, clothe yourselves with humility toward one another, for God is opposed to the proud, but gives grace to the humble. Therefore humble yourselves under the mighty hand of God, that He may exalt you at the proper time . . .
1 Peter 5:5–6

PRAY

Humility is required for every step of the rebuilding process. It takes humility for a husband to come to his wife, strip off "the good Christian" mask, and confess he's made a mess of their marriage. It takes humility for both sides to set aside their agenda and focus on listening to their spouse and making them feel heard. It takes humility for a man to admit he can't say no to temptation and his life is out of control.

It takes humility:

- For a wife to admit that God is working in her and wants her to change as much as her husband.

- For a husband and wife to admit they need the help of others and open up with their weaknesses. It takes humility to admit that either spouse has been employing dysfunctional communication methods, most of which were handed down by their family.

- For both sides to lay down their rights and make their spouse more important than them.

- For a wife to press through her anger and hurt and fight *with* her husband instead of against him.

- For the wife to forgive her husband for all of his sexual sin, lying, and the way he treated her.

- For a husband and wife to accept and affirm each other, in spite of the faults and mistakes of the other side and how they're been hurt.

Many marriages, regardless of whether sexual sin was involved or not, don't make it because neither side is willing to choose humility over pride. If the marriage lasts but pride is still on the throne, it's a walking corpse because there's no life, love, or joy.

At the core of the battle to choose humility is rebellion; the refusal to submit to God's way of life. It's insisting that my spouse must yield to what I want instead of saying, "Okay Lord, what do You want me to learn? How do You want me to respond?"

This workbook is a challenge because both sides must confront the ways they need to change and grow; pride must die so the marriage can live.

I'm right there with you. Hurtful words have stumbled out of my mouth many times; I knew I was wrong even as I was speaking; then it took an act of war with my flesh to get "I'm sorry" out.

After I apologize, Michelle is faced with a choice to forgive or hold a grudge. If I apologize but she doesn't release her anger, a rift develops between us. Resentment grips our relationship, and the downward spiral begins.

Humility opens the flow of grace. If I go to Michelle and confess there's a sin in my life that's kicking my butt, she shows me grace by receiving what I've shared without condemning or judging me. Her response encourages me to be transparent in the future and deepens my love for her.

"God gives grace to the humble." When a couple submits to God's ways, chooses humility, and puts their spouse's needs above their own, He weaves grace into the marriage. Grace could be as simple as a sense that "my spouse is my best friend." It could be an impression that God is with you, there is hope, and you're not alone. Grace could be peace in your relationship, or a wellspring of joy. It might come by the relief of a burden. Grace is loving and appreciating your spouse more, and gratefulness to God for the gift you have in your spouse. Grace can also be an exhilarating round of sex where you set the sheets on fire.

Sometimes all it takes is one act of humility to start a chain reaction of grace in your relationship. You could leave an unexpected note expressing love and appreciation for your spouse, prepare dinner and clean up after it, take the kids, or send your husband or wife away for a weekend with friends.

You may be just one act of humility away from opening new doors to peace, love, and healing in your marriage.

For today's action step, both sides are to pray and ask God to bring one thing they can do for their spouse to their mind that will bless them. Then follow through.

I know it would be easier for you to ask your spouse what they would like, but God knows your spouse better than either of you, including the way to their heart.

13

THE RIGHT WORDS

PRAY

Spouse A comes from a family of extroverts. They're fun to be around, and are a little on the loud side. They also have a habit of speaking impulsively, which can include jabs, barbs, insults, sarcasm, and put-downs. It's fun at first, they think, until someone is insulted and gets angry. The gloves come off, and soon everyone's trying to talk over each other. Chaos reigns; nothing is resolved.

Spouse B's family is the polar opposite of Spouse A; they're the introvert clan. Everyone keeps their emotions in check, as well as their words. Everyone is very polite, prim, proper . . . and sensitive. Everything must have its place and time. Problem is, they're a bit on the control freak side; when someone upsets the apple cart of their carefully planned structure they go into passive aggressive mode. Some withdraw into their shell, others pout. No one expresses concern that there's a growing rift in the family. Nothing is resolved, and their unhealthy communication patterns continue.

What do you think will happen when Spouse A and Spouse B get married? Spouse A, the fun side, brings their free-wheeling, fire-aim-ready communication habits to the table. It's not long before they say something that upsets Spouse B. Spouse B clams up and withdraws. Spouse A can't stand silence and lets loose with a barrage of sarcasm, jabs, and insults. Spouse B is simmering; they wish Spouse A would shut up and leave them alone. At this point, one of two things happen: (1) Spouse A, confused, goes and finds someone else to talk to. (2) Spouse A keeps talking until Spouse B explodes. Spouse A is shocked; but then picks up where they left off, and the whole thing falls apart.

Let's start with the standard God set in His word about what our communication pattern should look like:

> *Therefore encourage one another and build up one another, just as you also are doing.*
>   *1 Thessalonians 5:11*

> *But everyone must be quick to hear, slow to speak and slow to anger; for the anger of man does not achieve the righteousness of God*
>   *James 1:19–20*

> *. . . but speaking the truth in love, we are to grow up in all aspects into Him who is the head, even Christ . . .*
>   *Ephesians 4:15*

From these verses, we can see that we are to speak the truth in love, focus more on listening than talking, cool our anger-jets, and encourage each other.

Now let's look at some verses that apply to both spouses' faulty communication patterns:

Spouse A:

Like a madman who throws firebrands, arrows, and death, so is the man who deceives his neighbor, and says, "Was I not joking?"

Proverbs 26:18–19

When there are many words, transgression is unavoidable, but he who restrains his lips is wise.

Proverbs 10:19

Spouse B:

Indeed, there is not a righteous man on earth who continually does good and who never sins. Also, do not take seriously all words which are spoken, so that you will not hear your servant cursing you. For you also have realized that you likewise have many times cursed others.

Ecclesiastes 7:20–22

Therefore, laying aside falsehood, speak truth each one of you with his neighbor, for we are members of one another. Be angry, and yet do not sin; do not let the sun go down on your anger, and do not give the devil an opportunity.

Ephesians 4:25–27

God put the two of you together for a reason; He uses both

spouses to help the other with their weaknesses and blind spots. The problem comes when one side expects the other to communicate and think like they do and ignores what God might be saying to them through their spouse.

Jokes, jabs, or insults at our spouse's expense are not funny; neither are they loving. They should be eliminated from the marriage completely, as should threats, manipulation, rage, or guilt trips.

How we talk, our tone, is as important what we say. We can be technically right but spiritually wrong. For example, let's say my car has a flat tire. Michelle thinks it just needs air, but I've spotted a nail and know we need to get the tire repaired. We get into an argument; I angrily show her the nail, shout, "See, I told you so!" and insult her. Although I'm technically right, I've sinned against my wife by treating her harshly.

In God's economy, how we treat our spouse is more important than being right. Speaking the truth in love (Ephesians 4:15) is the order of the day, not insults, rage, or sarcasm.

If you're an extrovert like Spouse A, God gave you Spouse B to teach you to think before you speak, drop the put-downs and insults, and listen. As Proverbs 10:9 says, the more you talk the bigger the chance you'll dig a hole. Spouse B can model humility for you in this area; this makes them your teacher, helper, and completer.

If you're introverted like Spouse B, God gave you Spouse A to help you to toughen up a little. He also gave you Spouse A so you could learn not to be such a structured control freak, enjoy life, get out of your shell, and not wear your feelings on your sleeve. If you go into bitterness mode every time Spouse A blurts out something they shouldn't, you'll wear yourself out. This doesn't mean you should accept insults or jabs, but that you need to let some things go and allow Spouse A to be who God made them to be. They're just as flawed as you are; it's just that your sin is a little more concealed. This makes Spouse A your teacher, helper, and completer.

God also gave you your spouse to teach you to be an encourager; you get to practice grace and mercy at home so you can ingrain them into your character. It's been said we need to hear five encouraging words to offset one word of correction. Our words reflect what's in our heart (Luke 6:45); if you're always criticizing, judging, and demeaning your spouse it reflects an inner reality of misery and selfishness. If you focus on your spouse's strengths, how they're God's gift to you, and look for ways to encourage and build them up, the right words will follow.

For today's action step, discuss everything you've read today. Share your perspective with each other on how you see your spouse's communication patterns, and discuss your own. If your verbal repertoire has been sinful or damaging, make amends. Choose humility. Some get defensive when they're told their family of origin had dysfunctional or hurtful communication patterns. Set your pride aside and examine the truth. Then discuss any changes that need to be made.

PRAY

14

FINDING YOUR BEST FRIEND

This should be the easiest, and hopefully one of the more enjoyable chapters of this book. When a marriage blows up from sexual sin, all sense of friendship, fun, and adventure in the relationship can be lost. Today's assignment: date your spouse once a week for the next three months.

"Once a week for the next three months?! We have jobs, kids, families, and bills to pay. How 'bout once a month? We've been married for years and don't need it; it's not like when we were dating before we got married."

Yes, you need it.

Think back to when you first met your spouse. How crazy and over the top did you go for him or her? Remember chapter 6 of this workbook. What's the biggest priority in your life, second only to God? When's the last time you went overboard for your spouse? How do you think they would feel if you did? Loved? Cared for? Like they're a big priority to you?

A while back, Michelle and I were having a rough patch in our marriage; we'd drifted so far apart that neither of us knew how to get our relationship going again. It was so bad that Michelle wondered aloud whether our marriage had run its course. Our relationship was fading, and we desperately needed to make changes.

We started going out once a week. Money was tight, so we often met at our church café where meals were inexpensive. Occasionally we went to a theater where movies that have been out for a while were $1.00 for a ticket. Or we just walked around a mall and had fun window shopping.

The effect on our relationship was amazing. We started laughing again and having fun for the first time in years. The friendship we'd lost resurfaced; wounds started to heal. Life got better.

This came about from making a conscience decision that no matter what it took, we were going to make our marriage a priority and rebuild it. We both worked, had four kids, and little money, but we didn't let that stop us.

When my relationship with my wife is on the rocks, life sucks. Work's a chore, I want to hang my head at home, and feel like a poser in church. I don't sleep well. God made Michelle and me one flesh; we're not supposed to feel like everything's okay when our marriage is hurting.

Perhaps there is still resistance. "My kids/family/friends/church/office need me. I don't have time." Yeah, and so does your spouse; they come first. If your marriage is dying and your church is guilt-tripping you about not "doing enough for God," tell them no, or find another church. Yes, your kids need you, but don't you think your kids want to see Mom and Dad having fun together . . . instead of fighting, or worse? How about the office? I know we're living in tough economic times, but at some point you'll either need to make the time to date your spouse, or tell your employer you can't do 60-hour workweeks.

If you have kids, get a babysitter. If you can't afford one, the teens in your church may be willing to do it as ministry. Ask around to see what's available.

If money's tight, get creative. You don't need an expensive restaurant every week, just a place where you can get away from everyone and focus on getting to know each other.

When you go out, turn your cell phones off. Give each other your best; no distractions allowed.

If your kids are in school, meeting for lunch during the work-week is an easy way to avoid the need for a babysitter.

I strongly encourage you to plan a weekend away for the two of you. It will cost a little more, but every investment made in your marriage will provide an excellent return on your money and time.

When you're on a date, refrain from discussing kids, work, and family. Focus on each other. Share your dreams. Talk from the heart, but if possible try to set recovery topics aside. Have fun. Sometimes we can get so deeply immersed in support groups, counseling, and all that heavy stuff that we forget what it feels like just to unwind and have fun. Your marriage needs this.

Today's action step is to set a dating plan. Work together to find the best way to make it happen, and start this week.

15

RESENTMENT

Therefore, laying aside falsehood, speak truth each one of you with his neighbor, for we are members of one another. Be angry, and yet do not sin; do not let the sun go down on your anger, and do not give the devil an opportunity.

Ephesians 4:25–27

PRAY

Bitterness is a killer in marriage.

When a man or woman allows anger to fester for an extended period of time, the heart will eventually harden into bitterness. Once our heart is cold, it becomes nearly impossible to love our spouse. We may fake it and pretend everything's okay . . . for a while . . . but eventually the pus of our anger will ooze out and spill onto the relationship.

Perhaps one side stuffs their anger, while the other blows like a volcano. Both methods are unhealthy and can halt the communication necessary to heal the marriage.

Three steps are needed for lasting healing. The first is for the offended side to express their heart without attacking the other; afterward their spouse must grant forgiveness. If the couple has had unhealthy ways of dealing with anger in the past, it's important that they integrate new communication methods for the future.

Today, each side is to open up with resentment over any issues they have been harboring against their spouse, no matter how trivial. Perhaps working through this workbook has flushed out bitterness over an issue, or maybe it's been the white elephant in your relationship that you've been afraid to take on. Whatever it is, let's resolve it today.

Before you start, remember that your goal is to release your marriage (and your spouse, if they were hurt) from bitterness, not to be right or defend your turf. Embrace humility and focus on helping your spouse heal. If the issue your spouse brings up is something that seems petty or small to you, do not belittle them.

Some issues might require negotiation and time to work out. One side might need to compromise and agree to work to change in an area, while the other will need to be patient. Let God use your spouse to mold and shape you, especially in the area of humility and forgiveness.

Today have one spouse begin and share any resentment they need to discuss. Work your way through to resolution and forgiveness. Then the other spouse is to do the same. Keep going until both sides are finished.

In regards to the wife forgiving her husband for hurting her with his sexual sin, this topic will be discussed in chapter 17. For now I suggest you focus on the outlying issues.

16

THE GOD SEEKERS

"You will seek Me and find Me when you search for Me with all your heart. I will be found by you," declares the Lord, "and I will restore your fortunes and will gather you from all the nations and from all the places where I have driven you," declares the Lord, "and I will bring you back to the place from where I sent you into exile."
Jeremiah 29:13–14

A marriage is made up of two broken people, each with their own evil sin nature. One cannot heal the other, any more than they can fix themselves. Where many marriages get thrown out of balance is when one tries to change the other, instead of letting God do what only He can.

The Lord is your source of healing, freedom from sin, life, love, and lasting joy; He never designed your spouse to be your god. When both spouses see each other as they are, fatally flawed, and in need of Jesus, it frees them and gives God room to work in their spouses' life.

Which is one of the silver linings of your journey. When we have failed miserably and everything in our world has fallen apart, we often have greater clarity of our need for God than before. If we allow that understanding to propel us to a closer relationship with Him, He will draw near to us as He promised (James 4:8) and provide that which we have hungered for all along—a wonderful, life-changing, intimate relationship with the Creator of the Universe.

When a husband and wife discover the incredible joy of knowing the Lord, their marriage will change. God promised that if we seek Him with all our heart we will find Him. The key is to seek Him and set everything aside, even good things like a healed marriage, changed spouse, freedom from sin, or any other needs or wants. We can clutch our problems so tightly that they become our god; perhaps we tell the Lord we'll come to Him once He fixes our problems. He doesn't work that way. Many in the church go after God's hand of blessing; what He can do for them. Seeking His face, wanting Him alone, is about relationship; to know and experience Him. Through this entire process God may be saying, "I want *you*. I want first place in your heart. I won't compete with your spouse, problems, demands, or pride. Come to me and I'll fill you with new joy, love, and life that you never had before."

If you haven't started seeing breakthroughs or progress in your marriage, it may be that the Lord is using this to bring you to the end of your resources and pride so you'll make Him your only hope. If you have been making progress, that's great, but He still has an ocean's worth of love and grace to shower on you. You've barely touched your toe to the waters of grace; it's time to dive in head first.

For this action step, find a Christian retreat center, preferably one with no TVs in the rooms or other distractions, where you can have quiet, undisturbed solitude. Each of you are to go there, alone, for at least a 24-hour stay. If you can, two days is better. I suggest you don't bring anything more than your Bible, journal, a pen, and what is needed in the way of clothes and personal effects.

Leave your wants and needs at home. Forget about your spouse, kids, job, and problems. If the retreat has a phone, it's better to leave your cell phone at home, along with the laptop, iPad or any other electronic gadget.

After you settle in, I suggest you start by asking the Lord to show you what He wants you to do, then listen for the answer. He may bring a verse or book of the Bible to your mind, you may feel prompted to pray, worship Him, or He may want you to wait in silence.

If you've never done this before, it may take some time to calm your mind down and ease into silence. In silence, our spirit tunes into God's; His voice and promptings are easier to discern. Solitude, silence, and focused seeking on Him set the stage for an encounter you will never forget.

Be still, and know I am God.

Psalms 46:10

My soul waits in silence for God only, from Him is my salvation.

Psalms 62:1

Once the Lord gives you the first step, roll with it. If He shows you an area of your heart He wants to minister to, surrender to Him. Welcome anything He wants to do or show you.

Many Christians haven't discovered the deep joy of knowing God because they've never taken the time to seek Him in silence. Their morning quiet times are cluttered with thoughts of the day ahead, then they charge off without drinking deeply from the Fountain of Life. Now is your chance to encounter God. Give yourself permission to set everything aside; let it all go. I can tell you from the solo trips to a retreat I've taken that there's nothing like the joy of God's presence; He's spoken to me every time. The circumstances and methods are different, but the end result is the same; I've been granted the incredible blessing of reveling in His presence. It's always hard to leave, not because I don't want to go home, but because I've tasted Heaven.

After both of you have gone, share what happened, to the extent you feel comfortable. There have been instances when the Lord did such an intense, deeply personal work in my heart that I didn't share it with anyone.

17

THE SWEET SPOT OF FORGIVENESS

PRAY

Years after I exposed my porn addiction and adultery to Michelle, I asked her if she'd forgiven me for how I'd hurt her. She said she didn't know, and I asked if she would be willing to write a letter forgiving me.

She agreed; not long after Michelle read her letter to me. We were both in tears. She described how I'd hurt her, then told me she loved me and forgave me. It still amazes me; this was one of the most precious nights of our marriage, one I'll never forget. There's no way I could earn Michelle's forgiveness; she had to grant it willingly and with no strings attached.

Your marriage cannot completely heal until the wife forgives her husband. There's nothing a man can do to earn it; how can we make up for betraying our best friend and wounding them so deeply? We can't fix it or take back what happened. The only way through is for the wife to release her husband of his debt by forgiving him.

Granting forgiveness is as much about her healing as it is his. Maybe even more so. When she forgives her husband, she is releasing herself from anger and bitterness.

In today's action step, the husband is to begin by asking his wife where she is with forgiving him. If she hasn't forgiven him, he can ask her if she is ready and would be willing to. If she needs more time, the husband is not to try to force, manipulate, or guilt it out of her. She's being asked to pardon an enormous debt, and it must be something she freely gives from her heart, not out of coercion.

If she needs more time, her husband can ask her if there's anything he can do to help, then let it go.

If she's ready, she can verbally grant him forgiveness, or if she prefers she can put it in writing.

This is a big deal, so feel free to make something of it if you both want. You could go to dinner, or choose another venue. This is the ultimate act of love and grace in marriage, and may be one of the most intimate and precious moments of your relationship.

18

SEX

PRAY

Let your fountain be blessed, and rejoice in the wife of your youth. As a loving hind and a graceful doe, let her breasts satisfy you at all times; be exhilarated always with her love.

Proverbs 5:18–19

I like that verse.

The marriage bed is meant to be a fireplace of passion and excitement; *exhilaration*. The two of you should be lighting each other's fire and setting it ablaze. Marriage is the only place where God sanctions sex; married couples are told to have at it and enjoy. (See the book of the Song of Solomon if you don't believe me.)

When porn and/or adultery blow up a marriage, the couple's sex life is often decimated with it. Most wives don't want to be touched by a man who's hurting them.

Hopefully, the husband has been doing his part and experiencing freedom from sexual sin. If trust is reestablished, forgiveness has been granted, and your relationship is making progress, hopefully you've reintroduced sex into your marriage by now. If not, let's light it up.

If it's been awhile and you've had a long, hard road, this may feel awkward. This may be another step of risk and trust for the wife; she could be asking, "Can I really trust you with my heart again?" Meanwhile her husband might feel like Oliver Twist, sheepishly asking for something he's not sure he deserves . . . or might get turned down for.

Today, let's have a frank discussion about sex.

1. Talk about where both of you are with your sexual relationship. If it's been awhile and there's something in the way, bring it to the light. Is there an issue that needs to be worked through? Shame? Fear? Pain? Perhaps a little more time could be necessary for healing or trust to take place. Or maybe a few more dates are needed to prepare the fireplace. If, for some reason, you're not ready today, don't shelve sex for the long term. You need to work toward the goal of a vibrant sexual relationship and do what's needed to get there.

2. Discuss frequency. A little negotiation may be needed here. Talk about what would be healthy and reasonable for frequency and how you can make it happen. Men, it ain't happening every day, especially if you've got kids. On the other hand, once a month isn't enough (unless both of you are okay with it). Sex is a powerful force that bonds a couple together. To neglect it is not only deprive each other (1 Corinthians 7:5) but to rob your marriage of the emotional,

physical, and spiritual union that God designed sex for (let's not forget the exhilaration part). Sex is more than a physical act; it's an intense bonding force. You want your marriage to be as rock-solid as it can be; sex is the crazy glue that bonds it together.

Your sex drive may not match in intensity; it's not always the man with the stronger one. The partner with the lesser drive might need to work at having sex more than they prefer in order to bless their spouse. Meanwhile the one who wants it every night might need to ease up and realize they won't die without it; loving their spouse is still the main thing. To embrace humility in this area means both sides can't always have what they want; what is best for their relationship comes first.

Talk through your sexual relationship until you come to an agreement.

Pray and ask God to restore, refresh, and anoint your sexual relationship.

Then, you know what to do . . .

19

THE RETURN OF THE SERVANT-LEADER

When I saw their fear, I rose and spoke to the nobles,
the officials and the rest of the people: Do not be
afraid of them; remember the Lord who is great and
awesome, and fight for your brothers, your sons, your
daughters, your wives and your houses.

Nehemiah 4:14

Porn and sexual sin cripples a man emotionally and spiritually; his character atrophies. In this state most men check out when it comes to fulfilling their God-given role as the spiritual leader of the home.

I believe this is one of sexual sin's most insidious effects. The enemy wants to use lust as a Trojan horse that will infiltrate, corrupt, divide, and eventually take out your family.

Men, you are meant to be a warrior who will fight for your marriage and family; a man who will stand for truth and set God's standard of holiness in the home. You're to be an engaged husband and father instead of a passive wimp hiding in the garage. Your kids need you involved in their lives and the development of their character and spiritual growth. As their father your role includes firm yet compassionate discipline, holding your kids and telling them you love them regardless of their failures, building them up, and teaching them God's way of living by modeling it.

Our families, churches, and culture are dying for men of strong character who will step up and fight for their families. You must not check out any longer. Today you will move toward retaking your rightful place as the spiritual leader of your household.

The process began when you set your heart to work through the workbook with your wife. Every chapter has involved battle. If you've been patiently walking this journey with your wife, putting your pride to death, dealing with shame, fear, and wounds, and learning to care for her, you've been in boot camp. Everything you've done in this workbook has been preparing you to step into your warrior role of fighting for your marriage and family. Being a Christian warrior is not about yes-dearing your wife, but fighting with her and for her. Occasionally this may mean gently confronting her in love if she wanders off course.

When a man is distracted from his wife and children, his wife is forced to take up his leadership role by default. Some women may struggle with relinquishing this role back to their husband; this is another challenge of trust. Is he going to stay with it, or just show up a few times and check out again? Resentment because she had to be father and mother can thwart his attempt to lead once more.

Most women want their husband to be a strong leader. They welcome it when he charts the direction for their family, with her by his side. Leadership isn't dictatorship; his wife is his number one counselor and friend, with his best interests at heart. God will often use her as a kind of "second Holy Spirit" who helps him see his blind spots and avoid mistakes. A husband and wife who understand their roles and work together as one are a powerful force of light, love, and truth in their home, church, and nation. Satan has attacked your marriage because he knows that together you are a powerful force for the kingdom of God.

Some men may feel ashamed about resuming their leadership role, knowing their family has seen the depths of their sin and failure and how he's hurt them deeply. Part of this is a misunderstanding of the Christian way of life. We blow our testimony when we hide our sin and fake it; no one wants to follow a poser. Strong men and women of character are transparent with their brokenness, weaknesses, and failures. They don't hide because they're okay with being broken. Many believers have this backwards because they don't want to quit playing the game of pretending they're a "good Christian." Yuck. I admire men and women who have the courage to share their failures, and I bet you do too. Your kids will also respect you when they see your humility and courage; it will give them a picture of what a godly man or woman looks like and what they should aspire to be.

You and your family are at war. The enemy will do everything he can to keep you trapped in a prison of shame, just as he will attack your wife with doubt or resentment about the possibility of her husband resuming his leadership role.

So today, men, you're going to step up once more. You're going to fight against shame, fear, lies, inadequacy, and anything else the enemy has been hurling at you and your family. No more compromise, backing down, or apathy. Your wife will be right there with you. You will be a man worthy of your wife's respect.

For today's exercise:

PRAY

1. Talk about where the husband has been regarding his God-given role as the spiritual leader of your home. Wives, share any disappointments, resentment, or fear. Men, expose your heart and share any shame, sense of unworthiness, or fear. If you feel ashamed and are hesitant to take up your leadership role because of past mistakes, confess it.

2. Now let's turn the corner. Discuss what you want the husband's leadership in your home to look like moving forward. No two marriages are alike, so work at finding what's best for your family as opposed to how your parents did it or what others say. Talk about what you want the decision-making process to look like, what constitutes a major decision you should both discuss and agree on, and situations that don't.

3. Wives, most men desperately need to know you're behind them. When Michelle has my back I feel like I can do anything. Your support means more to him than anything else in this world (if not, it's because he was too self-absorbed to realize it). Tell your husband of the character and leadership potential you see in him. My wife sees my strengths as clearly as she does my faults. Your husband may have stopped believing in himself years ago, and all he needs is a few encouraging words from you: "I believe in you . . . here's why . . . here's what I see in you . . . I know you can do this." Take some time to share the strengths and gifts you see in him.

4. Men, your turn. Tell your wife that from today forward you will work to be her protector, best friend, servant-leader; a man worthy of her respect. This doesn't mean you'll get it right all the time; this is a learning process and you'll make mistakes. You are now stepping up and resolving to fight for the hearts of your family. Ask for her help where you need it.

5. Now fight for each other in prayer. Wives, ask that any residual shame in your husband's heart would be lifted, and that God will strengthen your husband to be the shepherd-warrior God has called him to be. Ask for the humility to allow him to make mistakes and step aside when you need to, as well as the courage to speak the truth in love if he wanders off course.

    Men, ask that God would restore your wife's heart completely from any damage that has been done. Ask Him to show you the priceless diamond you have in her so you can love her as He wants you too. Pour your heart out for her and pray blessings, grace, and love over her.

    If you have kids, pray for their healing and ask God to guard their hearts against the lies of this world. Ask for the wisdom, boldness, and grace to shepherd them and provide compassionate discipline where needed.

    Onward.

20

BLESSING YOUR SPOUSE

"See, the smell of my son
Is like the smell of a field which the Lord has blessed;
Now may God give you of the dew of heaven,
And of the fatness of the earth,
And an abundance of grain and new wine;
May peoples serve you,
And nations bow down to you;
Be master of your brothers,
And may your mother's sons bow down to you.
Cursed be those who curse you,
And blessed be those who bless you."

Genesis 27:27–29

The Old Testament blessing of a father was highly coveted by his offspring. Jacob stole for it; Esau begged for it. The blessing consisted of describing his character or actions, and invoking the father's vision for their future, which, hopefully, included a promise of future prosperity.

My kids attend Christian school. Every year, the fourth grade class puts on a father blessing event where dads publicly bless their child. It's an incredible, wonderful, emotionally charged time that touches the heart of everyone involved. I lost it when I blessed my first three kids; it was only with my fourth child that I was able to make through without coming apart. The kids are always beaming afterward; speaking the blessing over them is like anointing them with love.

It is no less powerful when a husband or wife blesses their spouse. In the midst of the grind of life and the pain of the recovery process, our need for the affection and approval of our best friend can get lost. Maybe we're afraid of getting hurt again. Or maybe the road has been so hard for so long that we've given up on the idea that our spouse could touch our heart with the love we experienced before marriage.

Today's assignment is to anoint your spouse with a blessing of love. Take some time alone and write out a blessing for them. I encourage you to pray before you begin and ask God to bring the words to your mind that will touch them. You might consider printing it on parchment or an otherwise classy style of paper, and framing it.

Then, read it to your spouse. You can read it in front of your family, or just the two of you. Make it a special event. I encourage you to look your spouse in the eye as you read the blessing. Don't hide behind the paper; connect with your soul mate.

To provide you with a structure and ideas for getting started, the following is a blessing I wrote for my wife:

Michelle—
Your name, which has French and Hebrew origins, means "she who resembles God."
When I think of God, the first thing that comes to

mind is His strength. You are a woman of incredible strength. You have persevered through many trials, not the least of which is the death of our second son. Many women would have faltered through the trials you have endured, but not you. You have shown amazing perseverance and strength over the years.

Perhaps the greatest characteristic of God is His love. From John 3:16 we know that love was the motivation behind the Lord sending Jesus to die for us. Your warmth, kindness, concern for others, and vibrant personality are like a magnet that draws others to you—and blesses them. You are skilled at building other people up.

The Lord said that "the greatest among you shall be a servant," and indeed, you have modeled the role of servant for your family, often going without thanks or appreciation.

So do you "resemble God"? Yes. For your perseverance, I believe the Lord will give you the blessings of an overcomer that He mentions in Revelations 2 and 3.

Today, I bless you in the name of the Lord Jesus with the following:

Michelle,

May the Lord bless you in the knowledge of your primary identity, which is that of a precious, beloved daughter of Christ.

May God bless you in the knowledge that He has

made you to resemble Christ, and may He help you to continue to do so, as He has in the past, for the rest of your life.

May the Lord bless you with double the love you have given to others, especially in your twilight years.

May the Lord grant you the blessing of knowing Him on an intimate level.

May the Lord grant you long life, so that you might see your children's children.

I love you.

Mike

21

DON'T HIDE YOUR LIGHT

This chapter is for those whose marriage has made significant progress. If your marriage is at place of healing and your relationship is in a good place, consider this a draft notice for service at the front lines. There are other couples who need your help.

Statistics show that two-thirds of Christian men are viewing porn and/or engaging in other sexual sin. A massive number of Christian couples are hurting, and need help. When it comes to sexual sin, many Christians keep their story concealed, not realizing that sharing what they've been through, what God taught them, and how He healed their marriage can be a tremendous blessing to others.

Men, the church needs guys like you who've broken free to share their story, start groups, and minister to others. Wives, there are many women who are dying for a safe woman to talk to who can relate to their situation. There are more resources for men than wives out there, often because women have a harder time opening up with something that's so deeply painful and shaming. The church needs women like you who have walked this path to share your story, lead groups, and minister to others.

Many people don't feel qualified for ministry because they don't have a title with letters after their name, or they haven't undergone training. You are probably more qualified than many counselors because you've lived it, persevered, and healed. You know what works and what doesn't.

A big part of ministry is showing up and saying "Okay God, here I am; work through me." Next is listening and making the other person feel heard, following the Holy Spirit's leading, and learning as you go.

We each have our gifts and passions; ask God what He wants you to do. Be flexible. You may have gifts you're not aware of because you haven't stepped out, put your faith on the line, and trusted the Lord to work through you.

Or maybe, your heart is burning as you read this because God is stirring your spirit.

We could always use help with Blazing Grace, both on the men's and the wives' side. If you might be interested in volunteering, please email me. My contact information is at the end of the book.

22

TWELVE REMINDERS

In closing, I'll leave you with the following:

1. Strive to live your priorities: God, spouse, children, then the rest. It takes consistent effort to filter out the chaff of life and home in on what's important. If you get distracted and wander a little, refocus. I constantly have to remind myself that "Husbands, love your wives as Christ loved the church" is my second biggest priority. Maintain your relationship and keep the doors of communication open.

2. Staying out of isolation by meeting consistently with other believers is meant to be our way of life, not a one-time thing we do in the recovery process. I meet with other Christian men for at least one lunch every week for accountability and encouragement. Make transparent fellowship with other believers a lifelong habit.

3. Date your spouse at least once a month. Go for a weekend getaway every three to six months, as finances and your schedule allows.

4. I like to go alone for an overnight stay at a Christian retreat every four to six months to re-energize my relationship with God. You'll be amazed at the difference this makes. Encourage each other to have extended periods of solitude with the Lord.

5. Pray together on a daily basis.

6. If you find you've drifted from each other, close the gap. Go back to doing the things you know you need to do.

7. Encouraging words make a big difference, whether spoken or written. Leaving a surprise card or note for your spouse is a great way to lift them up. I have a Post-it note on my computer at the office Michelle left that says "I love you Mike." It means a lot to me. I know Michelle likes cards and coffee, so occasionally I'll get her a greeting card and slip a Starbucks gift card in there. If you run dry on ideas, ask the Lord to bring one to your mind.

8. I think one of the hardest things in marriage is to accept all of our spouse's faults on a consistent basis. If an issue arises, pray for the wisdom and humility to know how to proceed. There will be times when God will want you to gently confront your spouse, and others where He'll ask that you to let it go and/or wait on Him. Or He might ask you to hug your spouse and tell them you love them (grace again . . . undeserved favor). Pray for wisdom before you respond.

9. Prayer is a game changer. Pray for your spouse every day. Pray for compassion and love when you don't feel like giving it. Pray for the will to do the things you know you need to. Encourage your spouse to pray. Suggest that the two of you pray if you're in a tough place or don't know how to proceed. Weave prayer into the fabric of your marriage and family.

10. Speak the truth in love when confrontation is needed. It will help the other side receive what you have to say.

11. Remember that your spouse is not your enemy; the devil will try to get you to bite on this lie when the going gets tough. Work *with* each other to solve problems. Proving you're right isn't as important as how you treat each other.

12. Make sex a priority. Set the sheets on fire!

Mike Genung can be reached at:

Blazing Grace Publishing
PO Box 25763
Colorado Springs, CO 80936

www.roadtograce.net

email@roadtograce.net

Your comments and questions are welcome.

See **www.roadtograce.net** and **blazinggrace.org**
for information on Mike Genung's other books, articles,
mp3s of the Blazing Grace Radio show,
information on future books, and more.

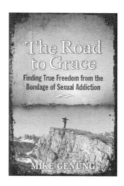

"I am so thankful I came across this book. I've read most of the highest rated books on sexual addiction and this is by far the best. Mike addresses the core issues we need to work through; this is a must read for anyone who struggles with sexual sin and accepting God's love and grace. Well done."
~Brandon

"I have just finished reading *The Road to Grace* and it is everything and more than I expected! I plan on rereading it starting tomorrow. Thank you; the book is changing my life."
~Joe

"Your book was amazing. I've read several sex addiction books and yours is the best. Your suffering and God's grace made this book powerful. It covers every aspect of sexual addiction from the steps to recovery to mending the marriage."
~Shelley Lubben

"Your book has done a great work of healing in my husband's life. We read it together. Each chapter he faces more of his past and heals those wounds. God bless you for your willingness to expose your life to everyone."
~K.B.

Features:

- Biblical methods for overcoming sexual temptation.
- Healing from shame.
- How to stop a masturbation habit.
- Dealing with the core issues that drive sexual sin.
- Understanding and receiving the love of God in the heart.
- Healing for wives.
- How to restore a marriage that's been scarred by sexual sin.
- Excellent for use in support groups.

Available at **www.roadtograce.net**

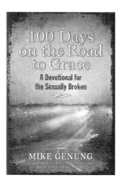

"One of our translators was really blessed by your book. It enabled her to look into her past and receive healing . . . she wanted you to know that it was a blessing for her."
~Phil P, Austria, director of a ministry that translated *100 Days* into German

"Your books enabled me to start turning the corner on a long road of darkness that enslaved me for 50 years."
~J.M.

100 Days on the Road to Grace: A Devotional for the Sexually Broken offers a collection of 100 powerful readings that expand on Mike Genung's first book.

Topics include:

- The path to freedom from porn and sexual addiction.
- Keys to rebuilding your character.
- Coping with emotions such as anger, depression, and fear.
- Rebuilding trust and bringing healing to your marriage and family.
- Bitterness and forgiveness.
- Breaking the bondage of self.
- Spiritual warfare.
- Revitalizing the relationship with God.
- Living a life that counts for eternity.
- And many more.

If you're hungry for God and want more than just freedom from sexual sin, this book is for you. Available at **www.roadtograce.net**